PROFESSOR
ON THE
ICE

PROFESSOR ON THE ICE

Robert E. Feeney

Pacific Portals
Davis, California

Puff
the Magic Penguin

Puff, the magic penguin, lived on the ice,
Where cold winds blow and there's lots of snow, a penguin paradise.
This song is the story, of a penguin and success,
How Puff made out in the world of men and found his happiness.

Whenever Puff was hungry, he wandered out to play
And frolicked in the garbage dump of winter quarters bay.
One day some silly USARP tried to catch him by surprise,
But Puff picked up some skua stuff and threw it in his eyes.

One day Puff saw the captain, who thought he'd have a laugh.
He sent Puff up to Chi-Chi as advisor to the staff.
Puff so impressed the admiral, that among some other things,
Puff came back to the captain with four gold stripes on his wings.

Well, Puff saved up his money, until he'd saved enough,
Booked passage on the Magga Dan and headed for the north.
He sweated and he worried, you'd sweat and worry too,
Until he joined his family at the San Diego Zoo.

Now Puff, the magic penguin, still lives at the zoo,
And fools around with Mrs. Puff, however penguins do.
She seems very happy as he nibbles on her leg,
And every day at two o'clock she lays a penguin egg.

Song sung at Christmas party, McMurdo, Antarctica, 1970. Apparently composed from numerous suggestions of Navy and USARP men. Chi-Chi is a Navy nickname for Christchurch, New Zealand.

Preface

The story that follows is of my experiences as an over-fifty university professor lucky enough to go to the farthest end of the earth to live and work outdoors with fish and penguins.

I hope it shows the interaction between a professor and his students and assistants in a project, and that it illustrates the fact that lecturing in a classroom is only a small part of the many facets of a professor's career—and that listening to lectures is only a part of a student's education.

My position in the seven-year program in Antarctic biology that I pursued was unusual in that I am more a chemist than a biologist, and a bench-laboratory professor rather than an explorer. I hope that my experiences will show others that changing the routine of one's career is possible for them as well as for me. I was able to do it without losing my position, which might not be too easy for some. But my experiences have allowed me to see that there are many others, both young and old, who have been able to do things that they had not previously believed possible. Some have even found new lives.

Nearly all this book was first composed either while in Antarctica or during the long trips to and from there. Parts of it were written or taped in the biology laboratory at McMurdo Station; parts of it were taped while spending nights alone in fish houses on the ocean ice. Still other parts were written in planes crossing the Antarctic Circle or while waiting for planes in New Zealand. The final rewriting and editing was done in my California home and Scott Polar Research Institute, Cambridge, England.

My seven-year Antarctic program was made possible only through the extensive help of many people. I hope that my deep appreciation of all those who accompanied me shows in the pages of this book. Much of the planning, preparation, and subsequent studies was done in the laboratories of the University of California at Davis by those who were not fortunate enough to go to the Antarctic. A primary and essential ingredient throughout the program was the continual help and guidance of the National Science Foundation. Among the many helpful individuals were Dr. George A. Llano, Program Manager of the Biology and Medicine Division, and Mr. Philip M. Smith and Mr. Kendall N. Moulton, both of whom were in the logistics and operational programs. Appreciation is also due the many individuals who provided permits for, and assistance in, collecting materials.

The writing of this book was materially helped by the editorial assistance of several individuals. Dr. James J. Dunning made suggestions on the initial draft. Mary and Horace Porter did extensive revision and rewritings. Charles A. Goehring did the final production.

Finally, the program and this book would not have been possible without the love, forbearance, and assistance of the three women in my life: my wife, Mary Alice, and my daughters, Jane and Elizabeth. They were the ones who had to get me off each year for six long visits, during which they rarely had any word of my activities or my safety. My wife was also a part-time home secretary, critic, and source of inspiration during the ten years from the start of the Antarctic program through the publication of the book. It is therefore to Mary Alice, Jane, and Elizabeth that I dedicate this book.

ROBERT E. FEENEY
Davis, California

Contents

PROFESSOR
ON THE
ICE

1
Committed

I am a biochemist. Until a few years ago my life was orderly and predictable. My status as a researcher was well established, and I enjoyed my life on the campus of the University of California at Davis with its challenge of herding bright young people through the intricacies of advanced research work. My wife and two daughters gave me comfort and happiness.

Yes, I was a contented, middle-aged professor, complete with gray hair, a slight stoop, glasses to peer over, and a well-equipped laboratory.

We were working on a research project involving egg-white proteins. We hoped, among other things, to unfold the secrets of why certain animals can be so similar in many ways and still have biochemical characteristics that are widely different, whereas other animals are closely related biochemically but themselves are different. We were sure we could find the answers to some of these questions through the study of proteins and enzymes.

We also wondered why various living organisms had totally different tolerances to cold and warm environments. Perhaps proteins and enzymes could provide an answer to this, too. Could our findings eventually result in an improved supply of the proteins man needs? Could they possibly help him survive under extreme conditions **1** of cold or heat or pressures of depth? Perhaps. One never knows where science will lead him. I certainly didn't!

We had gone about as far as we could go with our experiments with hen's eggs and other material available to us in the United States, when it occurred to me that we might try albatross or penguin eggs; they were large and probably available almost immediately after being laid, which was a characteristic important to our research.

The thought of using penguin eggs started a series of events which changed my life so completely that it is hard to recall what sort of life I lived less than ten years ago. Albatross or penguin eggs were so logical for my research that I immediately wrote to the Office of Naval Research in Washington. I wanted to know if they could pick up a few eggs for me the next time they were in Antarctica as part of the Navy's Deep Freeze program.

I was delighted to hear that the Navy would supply the albatross eggs with the help of their researchers at Midway Island, but they referred me to the National Science Foundation (NSF) for penguin eggs. After a series of letters, it became evident that the very fresh penguin eggs we needed could not be supplied. We would have to get them ourselves!

I was surprised one Friday afternoon a month or two later by a call from Dr. Donald E. Wohlschlag, professor of biology at Stanford, who asked what equipment I would need when I was in Antarctica. I not only didn't know what equipment I would need but certainly didn't intend to go to Antarctica! My way of life, my physical condition, my biochemical equipment, and Antarctica didn't seem compatible in any way.

The next morning, though, Dr. George A. Llano, head of the polar biology programs of the National Science Foundation, called me from Washington. He asked me to go to the next annual expedition planning conference at Skyland Lodge in Shenandoah National Park, Virginia. I assumed he wanted me to tell whoever was going to pick up the eggs how they should be handled. I accepted his invitation.

When I got to Skyland, however, I found that a "principal investigator" would be the man responsible for getting the eggs. He would also be required to go to Antarctica the first year of his research so that he would be knowledgeable about the problems there. NSF wisely assumed that if a researcher understood the problems, he would not ask the impossible. And then I found out that I was to be the principal investigator!

The remainder of the meeting was kaleidoscopic for me, but I recall talking about the remote possibility of going and thinking that my bum back would surely scratch me from the list. I also found that the group going "on the ice" the following austral spring and summer (October–February) was a sizable number of men. I had greatly underestimated the scope and size of the total operation.

The purpose of the Skyland conferences is to bring together all the people who are going to Antarctica the following season and brief them on the logistics, general operations, and problems they may expect to face. We also discussed who goes where, who gets what, and priorities.

One of the great aspects of the meetings is the participation of many of the really oldtimers and some of the "new oldtimers"—men who had been there only once or twice before.

At my first meeting I met one of the real oldtimers in an embarrassing way. The conference hall is in the main area of Skyland Lodge, but the dining facilities and offices are higher up the mountain, accessible only by hiking up a steep and narrow trail. A drizzling mountain rain had made the path slippery, and I slipped and fell into the brush in a spectacular display of ineptness for a prospective Antarctic explorer. An elderly but spry man who was following me quickly turned off the   **3** trail, reached down, picked me up, and set me back on my feet.

It turned out that he was Sir Charles Wright, the physicist on Scott's last expedition in 1912, who as leader of the rescue mission spotted the tent which contained the bodies of Scott, Bowers, and Wilson. Here, 52 years later at an age of about 75, Sir Charles, who had man-hauled sledges across Antarctica, was picking up someone about to go on the ice with planes, helicopters, and modern motorized vehicles. I suppose he was kind enough not to mention my clumsiness, because I was still designated as a part of the next Antarctic spring program.

Back in California, I had only about five weeks to prepare for the trip. Clothing was little trouble because the NSF representative in Christchurch, New Zealand, would fit us out with specialized Antarctic gear and clothing. But there was the U.S. Navy to reckon with.

The NSF is in charge of the Antarctic scientific programs and activities; the Navy handles all the supply services and housekeeping chores, with the senior naval officer as commander of logistics in the field. The Navy is also in charge of the medical facilities in Antarctica—and the physical condition of the men who go there.

One of the Navy requirements was a physical examination. I wasn't, I must say, looking forward to it, being by this time completely hooked on the idea of going. I was apprehensive because I had passed the mid-century mark, had led a rather sedentary life, and had acquired a few more lumps, bumps, and bruises than most people my age. Luck, bless her, intervened when I was permitted to be examined by a civilian physician. I'm not quite sure why this good fortune came about. Perhaps it was because of the last-minute rush, or it may have been the result of an informal appraisal at Skyland. If the latter, I was again grateful to Sir Charles for keeping mum about my slue-footed display on the trail.

If the Navy had checked me over, I'm sure I never would have made it. Here's what they would have found:

I was nearly blind in one eye, a consequence of a BB shot as a boy.

I had had severe amebic dysentery in the tropics during World War II and carried a residual unstable gut which made me watch my diet.

I had a chronic bad knee from high-school football. It had been severely injured again in World War II and had given out completely a year before, followed by extensive surgery on it a few months later.

I had experienced a painful lower-back problem for about five years and had been following a rigorous routine to prevent serious chronic disability. I did daily exercises, never sat on a soft couch or stuffed armchair, slept on the floor or on a perfectly flat hard bed, and wore a back brace when doing physical work.

I had contracted pneumonia shortly after the eight-month period of incapacitation caused by my knee injury and operation.

This inventory of physical ailments left me glum, but I felt agile enough to try to pass the physical.

I successfully arranged a two-week delay in my departure to Antarctica; I wanted time to shape up by following a concentrated program of physical development. Twice a day I swam for half an hour, and twice a day I ran up and down the stairs of Sproul Hall, an eight-story building next to my laboratory.

By the end of the five-week period I could make it all the way to the top and down again without turning my legs to rubber or losing my wind. Finally, there was help from my knee surgeon, who doubled as a back specialist. He thought, at first, I should not go. Yet when he saw the progress I was making in my exercise program, he admitted that he would go if he were housed in my physical body. After he had given me clearance on my knee and back, it became merely a matter of routine physical examination and request for waivers. Since my knee and back 5 problems were now "solved" and since I wore my back-brace only when engaged in "arduous exercise," was it really necessary for me to report all the other things on the examination form? Would the Navy want to be bothered with such trivia? The waivers were granted. I had passed!

2
On the Ice

It was mid-October when I arrived at Travis Air Force Base near San Francisco and reported to the Navy transportation desk with my equipment, nose drops, back support, aspirins, unguents, and bravest look. I was on my way! But to what?

The first leg of the journey was to Christchurch, New Zealand, with a quick stop in Hawaii. I sat next to a man who had been with Admiral Byrd in the thirties, and he made me feel less apprehensive about going down there at my age. His stories about the Antarctic of thirty years ago made me even more eager to see this strange land. Occasionally, during the long trip, I wondered about the wisdom of leaving my nice quiet home and laboratory, but I was glad I had made the decision.

Our converted Boeing 707 landed at Christchurch in the late evening, and I checked in at the headquarters of the U.S. Antarctic Research Program (USARP). The headquarters for the U.S. Navy Antarctic Support Forces are also there. Christchurch is where the Antarctic seems to begin. It's the last stop before going on the ice, and it's where we USARPs were issued our polar clothing and equipment. (If you are in the Navy, you talk about Deep Freeze. If you are with the NSF, you talk about USARP; in fact, you are called a USARP!)

Early the following morning, we were outfitted with heavy clothing (red jackets for easy identification on the ice, gloves, mittens, parkas, boots) and a lengthy list of instructions and hints for those of us who were to go on the ice for the first time. At 4 P.M. we assembled for our flight to Antarctica.

Ordinarily, stopovers at Christchurch are much longer because the usual bad weather delays flights between New Zealand and McMurdo Base, our Antarctic headquarters. This time, however, the weather was clear, so we left immediately. While waiting to board the plane, I picked up a bit of information that was somewhat perturbing to a greenhorn like me. At that time, all the planes that flew into McMurdo from Christchurch carried only enough fuel to go slightly over half the way and still return to Christchurch. Once the point of no return had been passed, a plane had to fly on to Williams Field at McMurdo regardless of the weather. Antarctic weather is infamous for its high winds and rapid changes; there are frequent periods when air transportation is impossible. The limited amount of fuel we were carrying was not comfortable to think about.

We took off at 7 P.M. in one of the great workhorses of Antarctica, the Air Force Hercules (or Navy C-130). Shortly before midnight the pilot announced that we had passed the point of no return and were going on to McMurdo regardless of the weather. I recall mumbling something that might have been a prayer.

The air traveler today is provided with reclining seats, cocktail lounges, lovely stewardesses passing out relaxing drinks, even piano bars. Our flight was different. The bucket seats were comfortable enough except that there wasn't any room to move around. Large and heavy equipment was packed in front of us and against us and stacked to the ceiling. When anyone wanted to visit the lavatory in the rear of the plane, it was necessary for each of us to part our legs so that he could step on the seats between our thighs. I was wedged between two sailors who, like me, were suffering from both claustrophobia and frequently pinched flesh from those who made the trip to and from the back of the plane. As far as I know there were no permanent injuries, but there were a lot of close calls.

About an hour before we were to land at Williams Field, we were told that the heat was being turned off so we could don our heavy clothing again. Try getting into a telephone booth with a friend, closing the door, then both of you changing into several extra layers of heavy clothing. You'll get a fair idea of the confusion aboard that plane! Somehow we made it.

We landed at 4 A.M. at Williams Field, where the landing strip is scraped out of the surface of the Ross Ice Shelf just off Ross Island. Those who were lucky enough to be near a window could see about two dozen bleak buildings huddled near the runway. That was Williams Field.

As the door opened the plane was filled with the intense brightness of the Antarctic sun reflecting off the ice. It was breathtakingly beautiful, with the temperature about −20°. Our breath seemed too thin.

And then I learned my first of many lessons in Antarctic survival.

At Christchurch we had been issued three different types of gloves: a large Antarctic or polar mitten, a work mitten with a wool liner, and a work glove with a wool liner. I had stashed the first two in my pack and, thinking that I was really wearing two gloves, wore the work gloves with the wool liner. This, I thought, would be enough protection for the short wait for the vehicle that would take us to the base.

By the time our packs and other gear were unloaded and we were being driven to the base, we had been standing in the wind and on the ice for over an hour. I was sure my hands were frozen. Obviously, I should have worn my work mittens, which would have allowed me to move my fingers around inside; better yet, I might have 9 used the large polar mittens, which will keep your hands warm no matter how cold it gets. It was only luck that my hands didn't freeze, but it was a good scare. It would have been embarrassing to report to the sick bay before I had even unpacked.

The trip from Williams Field to McMurdo took about half an hour in the snow vehicle, which bumped along at about 15 miles an hour. At the end of the ice road, we grunted up a small but steep hill directly onto the main road that led to the base. As we rode up the hill, someone pointed out that Observation Hill was directly in front of us and that we could see Scott's original hut about a mile to the west. In spite of the cold, I experienced a warm feeling. I knew that I was going to belong here.

During the austral summer, about a thousand Navy men are assigned in nearly even numbers to Williams Field and McMurdo Base. They keep the airstrip operating and maintain the planes and helicopters; the Navy men at McMurdo, their headquarters, perform all the housekeeping chores that are necessary to support the USARP scientists. In winter, which is summer in the United States, Williams Field is closed, and only about 150 Navy maintenance men are on duty at McMurdo. A tiny group of perhaps a half dozen USARPs conduct experiments during the long, cold, black, wintering-over months.

McMurdo Base is on the southern tip of Ross Island, where the Ross Ice Shelf meets McMurdo Sound. It is on approximately the same spot that Robert Falcon Scott established his jumping-off station when he fought his way to the South Pole in 1912. Scott also used it as a ship port and base for his *Discovery* (1901–1904) and *Terra Nova* (1910–1912) expeditions. It is one of the places nearest the South Pole where ships can land. Just over Observation Hill is the all-winter Scott Base, operated by New Zealand.

10   In 1964 McMurdo was a small all-male town of thirty or forty separate structures built on the hillside. Most of the buildings were Jamesway huts, which I will describe later, or prefabricated wood and metal structures. The streets were hard-frozen ice, rock, and soil in the winter, spring, and fall, but were usually muddy on summer days when the sun was warm and bright.

Antarctica's mainland is 60 miles west of McMurdo, and the jagged peaks of the Transantarctic Mountains scrape the sky in the distance. The base is protected to some degree from the bitter Antarctic winds by towering Mount Erebus and Mount Terror on Ross Island.

The ocean to the west stays frozen much longer each year than it does on the eastern side, and sometimes doesn't melt at all for several years. The 13,000-foot peak of Mount Erebus is only about 25 miles away and is an active volcano which issues a constant billow of smoke. Ross Island is, in fact, a heap of volcanic rocks. Mount Erebus adds not only beauty to the place but also a certain amount of élan. How many people live on the slope of an active volcano as we do at McMurdo? Might we go from the extreme of being frozen to that of being roasted? Everyone is too busy to worry or brood about these questions.

In addition to McMurdo, there are several other, much smaller all-winter bases, and as many as thirty field parties are scattered about Antarctica during the summer months.

After our 10-mile ride into McMurdo, we had breakfast and unloaded and stored the things we had brought. It took about two hours. Before I was able to take stock of things, it was 9:30 A.M. By the time I was able to get my containers and equipment together and discuss where I was going, it was lunch time.

Then I made my next mistake!

My NSF survival manual indicated we would be more comfortable if we wore heavy wool pants and high work shoes at the base, rather than the heavy full gear we had been issued; with only a block or two between buildings, **11** our warm parkas would provide sufficient protection for the short periods outside. So I doffed my heavy Antarctic clothing and put on ordinary G.I. wool trousers, a wool shirt, and regular high work shoes.

At lunch I joined a group of other men in my age group who had flown from Christchurch with me. They were members of a team making an inspection of the area and were to have a guided tour that afternoon in one of the snow vehicles. I asked if I might accompany them, and they obligingly included me. It developed that they were to have an elaborate four-hour tour that would take them several miles from the base. They all wore their heavy Antarctic clothing.

By the time we were back at the base, about 5 P.M., several parts of my body were numb and painful, including my rear end, thighs, legs, and feet. I decided that, when in doubt, I would always overdress rather than underdress.

After a late dinner, I returned dead tired to the USARP headquarters about 9 P.M. There, instead of receiving a billet, I was given the unexpected news that a helicopter would pick me up about midnight and take me across the island to Cape Crozier, a trip of about an hour. I would spend eight or ten days there living in a Jamesway hut while gathering penguin eggs. So once more I collected my equipment, changed into proper Antarctic clothing, and made myself ready for the helicopter. I made a quick visit to a carpenter shop, where I convinced the man in charge that I needed a piece of half-inch plywood for my research. It must be two feet wide by six feet long. The truth is, I had learned that the floor temperature in the Jamesway hut would be well below freezing; sleeping on the floor to keep my back straight was out of the question, so I had to get a bed board.

The ride to Cape Crozier in the early morning was calm and beautiful. It was my introduction to the
amazing serenity frequently found on the white conti-

nent. As you can see on the map of Ross Island, the actual distance between McMurdo and Cape Crozier is only about 50 miles. But the flight itself is considerably farther since the helicopter must skirt the edge of the island and attempt to keep over areas without crevasses in case an emergency landing is necessary.

Mount Erebus and Mount Terror were shining cathedral-like as we made the turn around the southern end of the island and headed toward Cape Crozier. Then, past the Ross Ice Shelf on the leeward side of the island, the sea was a magnificent sight. I had come from a hard, frozen land, but now I was looking down on the bluest ocean I had ever seen. Icebergs were everywhere, in the far distance I could see the dome shape of Beaufort Island, and behind me rose the icy sheets of a mainland mountain of ragged peaks and precipices.

I fell in love with Cape Crozier at first sight. Now I can say, after many lengthy visits, that I have experienced more beauty and serenity there than at any other place I have ever been.

In spite of the magnificent scene, the Jamesway hut that appeared as we landed looked lonely and forbidding. But I was wrong!

I was met by the two occupants of the hut, Robert C. Wood and William Emison, both of Johns Hopkins University. Within a week's time I knew these men intimately and acquired a deep affection for both of them. Bob Wood's path has crossed mine many times since then, and he has become one of my close friends. One of the great treasures of being on the ice is the friendships that develop there.

They guided me down the hill, ushered me into the hut, and helped me stow my luggage. We chatted for awhile, and they helped me put up my cot and unroll my sleeping bag. They did not question my board for the cot. At about 6 A.M. I felt a deadening fatigue settle over me, and I realized that I had had only a few hours of sleep (in Christchurch) over a 72-hour period. This was aggra- **13** vated by the loss of sleep my last night at home because of excitement and the many last-minute preparations.

My last memory of the previous three days was of these two fine young men talking to me as I dozed off to sleep on my first night on the ice.

3
Cape Crozier

Twenty-six hours later I woke up and looked at my quarters on Cape Crozier—a Jamesway hut.

It was about 12 feet wide and 20 feet long. The floor and ends were made of wood, with a small window at each end. The roof and sides were padded canvas laced to a frame of wooden arches. Overall, a Jamesway hut looks like a World War II Quonset hut made of "temporary" material. Nevertheless, they are strong and tough.

In the middle of the hut was the important diesel-fuel heating stove—a piece of equipment with which I became very familiar during subsequent years in the Antarctic. It operates by the simple process of dripping fuel into a pan at the bottom of the stove; the fuel then burns, warms the hut, and the smoke goes up a stovepipe.

A small table at one end of the hut served for dissecting birds, working on electrical equipment, writing letters, preparing and eating food, and anything else a table was needed for. We would almost always wipe it off between uses.

Just behind the table was the cooking area, a small wooden shelf that held the two-burner Coleman gasoline stove that most of us know from camping in the United States.

The other end of the hut contained cots, one on each side of the door, with a little space between the cots and the end of the hut for insulation against cold. As many as six people can sleep in the hut, with double-decker cots on each side and two single cots beside the table and cooking shelf; the single cots must be taken down every morning, however, to make room to move around. When six people sleep in a Jamesway hut, it is almost as crowded as it was in the plane from Christchurch to McMurdo.

Bob Wood and Bill Emison had made breakfast, and after eating it eagerly, I pulled on my heavy Antarctic clothing and went outside for my first good look at Cape Crozier.

From our hut on the lower slopes of 10,600-foot Mount Terror, I could see how the mountain cascades into the ocean. It was a crystal-clear day, with a few fleecy white clouds lazing in the distance above the placid sea with its floating icebergs. I learned later that a calm sea can change rapidly into the roughest of all seas, with sheets of sea ice or large icebergs crashing against one another with the noise of an artillery barrage. Within a few hours, the ice can move in from far out at sea or around the end of the island. But this day was calm, serene, and beautiful.

The most thrilling sight of all was the thousands of Adélie penguins directly between us and the sea. The hut had been placed to be as close to the rookery as possible, but out of the nesting area. As we stood in front of the hut, we could see more than a hundred thousand penguins at one time—a third of the rookery population. The constant murmur I heard was a summation of all the noises penguins make, from small semiclucking noises to those resembling the growl of a small dog.

As I looked eastward over the ocean, I could see the majestic Ross Ice Shelf clearly visible about four miles away. It is a flat slab of ice, about 600 feet thick where it rises straight up out of the ocean; it covers an area equivalent to the size of Texas and Louisiana combined. Pieces break off occasionally and float to sea as large flat icebergs, which sometimes have to be pushed out of the way of the ships that come to McMurdo.

The Ross Ice Shelf, the nearest corner of it at least, is the Cape Crozier emperor penguin rookery. The emperor penguins are larger and more formal appearing than the Adélies and consider themselves to be much more important. But the Adélies do a lot more living!

Behind the hut was the helicopter landing pad, a small, nearly level spot about a hundred yards up the mountainside. I walked up the slope about half a mile and saw the upper part of Mount Terror towering above everything. It held a strange fascination for me.

I could also see the precautions that had been taken to protect the hut against the winds. Strong guywires had been secured into the permafrost of the volcanic soil. The entire area was either volcanic ash or volcanic rocks varying from pea size to large boulders, the result of the many eruptions of Mount Erebus less than forty miles away.

Just behind the hut, facing the slope of Mount Terror, were four 8- by 12-inch beams 12 feet long, surfaced with heavy plywood to form a wedge like a huge snowplow. The wedge was a wind deflector, erected to protect the hut from the fierce winds that roared down the slopes of the mountain. The guywires were embedded at the back of the hut as well as in the front. Large piles of rock had been gathered to fasten the main wires to the ground. Those in front, which were on a greater slope, were fastened in a pile of ice-covered rocks. This mound of ice was continually being replenished by the wash waters from the hut and the liquid excreta from the inhabitants of the hut.

The central cable to the front of the hut was the lead making it possible, when nature called, to go out to the rocks in heavy winds. In the fiercest winds, sometimes reaching twice the force of hurricanes, even this was impossible, and all such personal necessities had to be **17** taken care of inside the hut. Disposal had to wait until the winds abated a day or two later. Our other essential facility was 30 or 40 yards from the hut. It was a thronelike affair with the back boarded to protect us from the winds, but the front of it provided the user with a beautiful panorama of the penguin rookery and the ocean.

My tentmates explained that housekeeping chores were, mainly, cooking, cleaning, and dishwashing. The gathering of water was actually the gathering of snow to be melted on top of the heating stove. Sometimes getting snow was not an easy task; it had to be brought in from behind the hut, with the volume of water no more than 25 percent of the volume of snow. It seemed to take an endless number of buckets of snow to get enough water for any use at all.

The men at McMurdo had it easier. They gathered snow with heavy mechanical snow-moving equipment and stored it in huge hoppers at the side of each building.

Strange as it seems, dependence on snow often caused serious water shortages because, by the end of summer, snow usually becomes scarce; sunshine melts it, snowfalls lessen, and winds blow it off the mountainsides. Antarctica, despite our mental picture of it as having constantly falling snow, is the most arid of all the continents. There is very little precipitation as we know it; the snow mostly just blows from place to place.

Our food was chiefly steak and frozen or canned vegetables, fruits, and other commodities that are easy to transport, convenient to store, and solidly nutritious.

Other chores peculiar to life in the Antarctic include recording the daily temperature and wind velocity and transmitting a complete weather report by radio once a day. The transmission (the Sched) is always sent, if possible, when all members of the group are present, since messages about other matters may also have to be sent to McMurdo. Sometimes we could not make any radio contact at all, and at other times our contact was unidirectional. Often, when direct communication was impossible, messages could be relayed through another station.

18

Transmission of radio messages necessitated carrying the gasoline generator from the hut to a place somewhat removed and using it to supply power for the radio. The generator was stored in the warm hut to make starting easier, but it had to be moved before starting because of the fire hazard.

Fire is one of the great dangers in Antarctica, mainly due to high winds and the lack of water away from the open ocean. Winds greater than 100 miles per hour are common, and they whip about with such rapidity that they can fan small flames into devastating conflagrations in seconds. The result can be total destruction of personnel, shelter, and supplies.

Dr. William J. L. Sladen, the eminent ornithologist from Johns Hopkins University and the professor with whom Wood and Emison were associated, experienced such a fire while with a British team in the 1950s. Two of Sladen's three tentmates were burned to death and most of their supplies lost while he and the other survivor were away doing field work. His terrible personal experience had a lasting effect on the attitudes of all of us. I had met Bill Sladen for only a few minutes while at the Skyland briefing meeting. Now I wanted to get to know him well.

We provided some insurance against the hazards of fire by storing an emergency cache of clothing, food, and a tent far enough away from the Jamesway hut so that there would be little danger of it being consumed by a fire originating in the hut. When I stored my materials in the cache, I had no idea we would come very close to needing them in a few days time!

4
Meet the Adélies

As soon as I settled my routine, I set to work with the Adélie penguins, which had charmed me so much from a distance. I really didn't know much about them at that time—not even how many eggs they laid. What I know about them now is the result not only of my own observations but of reading and talking to friends in Antarctica who have studied them. People who have worked with penguins would rather talk about penguins than about people.

There are two species of penguins—the emperors and the Adélies—at Cape Crozier.

The emperors are over three feet tall and weigh from 65 to more than 90 pounds. They have bright orange-yellow ear patches, dark gray backs, and black heads. They are impressive in their regal stuffiness, but they are dull! The Adélies, on the other hand, are exciting and excitable, demonstrative, imaginative, silly, and lovable.

To me, these appealing Adélies are the most delightful and entertaining creatures in the animal kingdom. They look and act like people. The Adélie is a raffish, argumentative fellow whose philosophy seems to be, "When in trouble or in doubt, run in circles, scream, and shout." He is usually kind to his companions, although he's also quite willing to steal them blind when he thinks he can get away with it!

Adélies show happiness, anger, worry, affection for each other, deviousness; when it comes to wooing, they are romantic, tender, and loyal. Anatole France was so fascinated by penguins that, in his delightful satire of the human race, *Penguin Island*, he convened heavenly court to consider endowing the penguin with a soul.

When we see a penguin waddling about it's easy to assume that he is a bumbling, stumbling, outlandish clown; but when we see him in the water, beautifully coordinated and swimming with incredible speed and grace, it's an entirely different story.

Adélies weigh about 12 pounds, depending on the amount of stored fat, and are approximately 15 inches high. Their bellies and throats are white, and their backs and heads are black with a little grayish tinge at the tips of their feathers. The black extends in a band around the neck, giving the bird the appearance of a person wearing a black hood.

They breed their young on land but are far more at home in the water than ashore. Their short tails are used as a balancing device when they sit and as a rudder when they swim. They stand up straight because their feet are placed far back on their bodies, rather than at a point midway as is usual in birds.

The Adélie spends only about a third of its life on land, but even part of that time is spent eating at sea. Two-thirds of the Adélie's life is spent away from its nesting area, heading northward as the winter sets in; it returns punctually to Cape Crozier (in the case of the birds at this rookery) each Antarctic spring, about November 1.

Stormy weather doesn't stop the penguins. Their instinctive, fiercely earned punctuality has a twofold reason. Their chicks, which will hatch in the spring, must be mature enough to go to sea before winter sets in near the end of February. The adults must have time to molt **21** and regrow feathers so they will be able to go to sea once more. Any delay in this sequence will result in death for the small birds, the adults, or both. Thus life itself depends on ocean-going readiness before the change in the weather makes it impossible.

There have been a few sightings of penguins floating on the loose ice at the northern periphery of the winter ice pack; but since ships do not normally venture into the pack at this season because of thick winter ice and darkness, we really have little idea of the hardships penguins must live through in winter.

Watching the Adélies beginning to show up at Cape Crozier in the early spring is exciting. They arrive in droves of thousands, approach the edge of the ice, and catapult themselves in a beautiful arc out of the water and onto the ice where they start waddling inland. Usually they are able to swim most of the way to the rookery, although there may be patches of ice they will have to walk across or dodge in their swimming. Some years there may even be vast stretches of solid ice across which they must walk. They still manage, somehow, to reach the rookery at nearly the same time each year. The struggle to walk on the land is hard on them, since they expend considerably more energy in walking than in swimming.

One of the miracles of the penguins is that each seems to return to the exact location where he or she nested the year before. Each, furthermore, seems usually to find its former mate, even though the mates do not necessarily arrive together. If the interval between arrivals is as long as four or five days, however, there are problems. Faithful as penguins are, they cannot be very late in their business of raising a family. After a few days without a former mate, a penguin must find a new one.

A penguin rookery consists of a place to land from the sea and rocky sites where the individual groups or colonies of breeding birds can make their nests. Most of the space in a colony is taken up by nests, separated only by buffer zones large enough for a penguin to move freely in defense of his nest. The nest and its surrounding zone is the territory the penguin couple will defend against encroaching neighbors.

A penguin has two major enemies: the skua gull ashore and the leopard seal when in the water.

The skua makes frequent attempts to steal the eggs or the young penguin chicks, but penguins are usually successful in fighting him off with beaks and flippers.

The leopard seal cruises menacingly along the edge of the ice where the penguins enter the water. His sharp fangs can quickly grab a penguin and crash its body against the surface of the water, literally skinning it. It is not a pretty sight to see! When a penguin makes his way to solid ice, on the other hand, he can waddle faster than the seal can maneuver out of water.

Soon after arrival, the penguin, usually a male, starts building a new nest or repairing an old one. If he is joined by his mate of former years, there is a period of recognition and communication, with intermittent nest building. If there is no female, the male will usually begin building the nest by himself. He will gather small rocks in his beak, carry them to the nesting site, and push them around with his bill and feet until he has created a small pile of rocks with a concave area in the center. If he thinks he can get away with it, he will try to steal stones from his neighbors. If he gets caught in the act—and he usually does—a real donnybrook starts, with flippers beating and beaks pecking; the screaming and fighting that goes on is hilarious to watch.

While gathering rocks, the penguin will pause occasionally and go through various acts of communication. One, called the ecstatic display, is considered to be an announcement by the male that he is ready to set up housekeeping. Once the male is joined by either his former mate or a new one, the pair will work together to complete the nest. After initial communication, courtship, and nest building, mating may occur.

The mating acts of penguins are similar in many

respects to those of other birds incapable of sustained flight, but penguins are more affectionate. The main difference, of course, is that penguins mate during just a few weeks in the Antarctic spring. The first two or three weeks in November are wild with squawks, splutters, screams, and hubbub. In the actual mating process, the male mounts the female, who lies on her abdomen while twisting her body around to maintain a beak-to-beak "kiss."

The Adélie lays two eggs, the first within a week after the birds arrive at the nest and the second two to five days later. In the interim, the first egg is kept from freezing either by the female or the male, but it is not incubated until the second egg arrives. In this way the two eggs will hatch at about the same time. The eggs are hidden beneath the bird in a fold of loose abdominal skin. During the incubation period, the penguin rolls the eggs over and over to maintain constant warmth.

A day or two after the second egg is laid, the female goes to sea for food. After all, she has had a courtship, helped build a nest, made violent love, and laid two eggs weighing about half a pound, or five percent of her body weight. So now the male takes over the incubation and protection of the eggs.

It seemed mean of me to take eggs from these wonderful birds, even if I had to for scientific reasons. But that's why I was there, though I must say the job wasn't easy.

With the help of my friends, I developed a technique for getting the eggs from the penguins. Even when the birds were standing, I couldn't tell which were holding eggs in their pouches. By lifting them by their rumps and holding them upside down, it was possible to remove the eggs. Penguins become disoriented when upside down, and after being righted again, are slow to attack. Nevertheless, the theft was accompanied by shrieking objections and frequent attacks on my rear end by sharp beaks. Penguins are not only vociferous but scrappy. They also, by the way, smell to high heaven! And so does anyone who pals around with them as I did.

In the first three days at Cape Crozier I gathered about 50 eggs, almost enough for my research needs.

5
First Storm

I was fortunate to have almost finished my egg-gathering chores quickly. On the third day of my stay at Cape Crozier, a storm roared down the slopes of Mount Terror, as Wood and Emison had said it would. Within two hours we were housebound.

The wind thundered and tore at the canvas of the hut with such ferocity that it was impossible to carry on a conversation. We had to shout to understand each other, even partially, at distances of two or three feet. The storm lasted for three days. It did not stop as abruptly as it had started, for on the last day there were short periods of relative calm followed by turbulence as great as at the height of the storm. I discovered that this storm was typical in its pattern, and in later years I valued the stormy times for reading, writing letters, working on research data, or taking naps. Long sleeps were not the rule, however, because of the constant necessity of watching the effects of the storm on the hut and of working to keep it safe.

At the height of this particular storm, we nearly abandoned the hut for fear it would be torn from its moorings. This would have meant donning our heaviest clothing and attempting to hole up some distance away, wherever we could get protection from the wind by lying flat on the ground or huddling together on the hillside. The reason we considered abandonment was simply that our lives would have been imperiled if the hut had started to blow away.

We had already put out the fire and donned our outer clothing when Bob reappraised the situation and decided to try to save our shelter. Bob and Bill made two trips outside and, clinging to ropes and guywires, lashed together parts of our hut that had already been torn apart. They had to tie themselves to the hut at times to keep from being blown away. For the moment, at least, abandoning the hut became unnecessary, and we resumed our storm watch.

A short time later, a totally unexpected event might have meant abandoning the hut for good had our response been delayed only a few seconds.

I had been gazing, with some boredom, at the heating stove. Suddenly the smokestack began to move slowly upward in a steady but accelerated movement similar to the launching of a rocket at Cape Kennedy. Had I been more experienced, I would have known immediately that the wind, having gotten below the flanges of the smokestack outside the canvas, was battering and lifting the stack from the underside. My shout brought a concerted and simultaneous grab for the stack, which we caught just before it went out through the opening in the roof. Had we not saved it in time, the roof opening would have been a weak and vulnerable entry point for the attacking wind.

As if we didn't have enough trouble at this point, the stove ran out of fuel, which meant switching the fuel line from one diesel-oil drum to another outside the tent.

A serious hazard in Antarctica is spillage of petroleum products on clothing or skin. Petroleum, when extremely cold, can freeze the surface of the skin on contact. In a raging wind of 100 miles per hour, petroleum whipped around in the air can freeze the face and eyes instantly. Bob was, as always, a patient teacher and han- **27** dled the problem with consummate skill. I soon learned the hazards of such an apparently simple task.

During brief lulls in the storm, we made forays from the hut and, clinging to the guywires, performed whatever maintenance work was necessary. On one of my trips outside, the thundering wind suddenly resumed, and I heard a ripping sound somewhere behind me. With one arm around the guywire and stooped to reduce wind pressure, I turned to see a huge beam hurtling at me. Instinctively, I flung myself flat on the snow and watched it tumble over me at incredible speed. I later found that the wind had destroyed the windbreak behind the hut and that the beam was part of the ruins. It was the size and girth of a railroad tie, but more than twice as long, and weighed far more than I could possibly have lifted. I suppose the wind must have gotten under the heavy plywood and given it a lift before it took off. The only damage I suffered was a slightly sprained wrist, a bruised head, and a spectacularly dirty parka. I had fallen directly into the spot where we emptied our slop and other unmentionable things!

In moments of freedom from the struggle for survival during the storm, I broke the eggs I had gathered, separated the contents, and made observations on individual eggs. All the samples of eggs whites and yolks were placed in individually labeled bottles and frozen by placing them outside of the hut. After the storm had ended, I had only a few samples still to get, which I managed to do without difficulty.

The day came for my return to McMurdo from Cape Crozier, exactly eight days after my arrival. It was a bright, sunny, calm day, with no resemblance to the ferocity of just three days earlier. I felt as though I had lived at Crozier for six months.

When the helicopter landed, I rushed forward to get aboard. I stopped in my tracks when I saw a group of five visitors, all in neat clean clothes, sitting together in the helicopter like stately emperor penguins, but with red coats and black pants rather than black coats and white fronts. They had come to Cape Crozier to see the penguins.

So the five clean coats and the one torn coat, covered with a patina of penguin dung and slop, all went back to the hut for a cup of coffee before leaving for McMurdo Base. Our visitors had just participated in an organized series of trips and visits to many places in Antarctica. I had been rolling in the muck of a penguin rookery, and I smelled like it.

I envied them at first, but as we were flying back to McMurdo and I was telling them about my week at the Cape, I realized that it was I who had been the lucky one. I knew then that I wanted to continue my work in Antarctica.

My departure from Antarctica was swift and uneventful. Within half an hour of our arrival at McMurdo, I was having a highball at a farewell party for our visitors. An hour after that I was aboard the Hercules again, headed for Christchurch. But it was a different ride back. As I looked out the ports of the nearly empty plane, I felt at ease with the world. I had lost my fear of the unknown Antarctica. What little uneasiness still remained was dispelled by the realization that there was no point of no return on the way back.

6
New Zealand

One of the bonuses of involvement in the Antarctic is stopping over in New Zealand. A few are lucky enough to visit Australia and enjoy the wonderful hospitality of that country, too. On this first trip I was fortunate enough to visit both countries on my return from the ice. I had arranged for a two- or three-week visit before returning to the United States.

I hoped to obtain both blood and eggs of some of the New Zealand penguins, which are quite different from the Adélies and emperors of Antarctica. I also hoped to get an egg of the rare New Zealand kiwi. The kiwi is about the size of a chicken, has a long beak and a sort of hippie haircut, and once nearly became extinct. I thought if I could get these materials from New Zealand and compare them with my findings in Antarctica, I might find exciting differences and similarities for my research.

But my main reason for going to Australia was to obtain blood samples from the flightless emu, another highly protected bird; I felt that the sooner I could find out about the biochemical makeup of this extremely interesting species, the better. I also knew that I should have to present a strong argument to convince the New Zealand and Australian governments that I should have permission to get what I needed. I was right!

The people of Christchurch, which is on the South Island of New Zealand, have long been familiar with Antarctica and the men who have faced its challenges. It was here and in the nearby port of Lyttelton that Captain Scott and many other British and New Zealand explorers outfitted their ships for their Antarctic explorations. It is the nearest to McMurdo of any civilized land with good facilities, and although weather is almost always foul around the Antarctic continent, Christchurch is a far better place to depart for the ice than, say, Punta Arenas (at the tip of Chile), which involves crossing the dreaded Drake Passage.

Another good reason for using Christchurch is that New Zealand has laid claim to the pie-shaped Ross Dependency, which includes most of the Ross Sea and the Ross Ice Shelf; its apex is the South Pole. The Ross Dependency also includes Ross Island, where McMurdo is. Australia also claims that part of the mainland which borders on McMurdo Sound.

These claims, like those of many other countries, cannot be enforced until 1995 under the terms of a unique treaty made by twelve nations in 1958. It was agreed under the treaty that Antarctica would be a temporary international territory. No country could lay claim to any portion of it for thirty years. The areas that each country had claimed were recognized, but in the meanwhile the continent was reserved for scientific studies and exploration. No weapons testing may take place there; all the signing nations must notify each other about expeditions to explore the wild country; nuclear explosions are prohibited; and any nation may inspect the installations established by any other country. Strangely enough, the signing countries often have completely opposite political philosophies, as in the case of the United States and the Soviet Union. But the treaty works and works well. We often visit the Soviet bases, and they exchange information with us. I believe that the breakthrough for peace in the world may well be through the community of interests of scientists.

31

One of the terms of the treaty is that none of the signing nations must give up claims to territory made before 1958. When the treaty ends in 1995, it may be reconsidered. In the meantime, we scientists get on splendidly together. It's too bad the politicians can't follow our lead!

New Zealand has a base on Ross Island; their Scott Base is only three miles from our own at McMurdo. Many of the New Zealanders' supplies are flown or shipped to McMurdo and trucked over the hill to Scott by the U.S. Navy.

When I returned to Christchurch from McMurdo in the early morning, I was greeted by the longtime USARP representative, the incomparable Eddie Goodale. Eddie could have confined his work to his assigned duties, which were to see that the men going on the ice were outfitted, assigned to quarters, and given instructions on how to live in the Antarctic, and to handle the ever-present paperwork that accompanies the movement of men and equipment. Eddie, like most USARP representatives, did all that and a lot more. He was in his early sixties, and he herded his charges about like a mother hen. He had greeted us enthusiastically when we had arrived on our way south, taken us through customs, carried our baggage to the waiting trucks, and seen that every detail was taken care of. He went about his self-imposed extra duties with exuberance and contagious good humor. Everybody was a personal friend of Eddie's.

It wasn't until later that I recognized why he went to all this extra trouble. Eddie was an old Antarctic hand who had been with Admiral Byrd in the 1930s and with the International Geophysical Year (IGY) operation in 1957 and 1958, the first really major international scientific research program. Eddie never lost his intense desire to be part of any Antarctic operation, even if it was only to unload baggage. I now understand his feeling. It is difficult to describe the satisfaction of belonging to the **32** fraternity of Antarcticans. That morning, however, I hadn't yet grasped all this, and I marveled at Eddie's obvious enjoyment in helping. His position as a USARP representative was an important and respected one—the baggage handling was his own idea. In subsequent years, Eddie herded me through Christchurch many times and never changed. I am sure that it was with great reluctance that he finally retired to a farm back in the United States. Eddie Goodale is one of the great men of Antarctica.

I turned in my Antarctic gear and was assigned to U.S. Navy quarters at the airport. It was 3 A.M., but I headed immediately for the shower, where I luxuriated under an endless blast of hot water for half an hour before turning in. I slept for twelve hours.

In the afternoon I was awakened by the sound of young men chatting with girls right under my window. It sounded so pleasant and normal that I shaved and started to get dressed, thought of my age, changed my mind, and took another long shower. Sometimes creature comforts are undeniably man's greatest joys.

After a civilized and delicious dinner, I packed and boarded the packet boat that ferries men and supplies from Christchurch to Wellington, New Zealand's capital, on North Island. I saw the stars for the first time in two weeks, felt the warm wind on my face, and watched the lights of the shore pass by until I headed for my stateroom. In the morning we crossed the notoriously turbulent Cook Strait and docked in Wellington Harbor amid the foothills of the Tararua Range.

My reason for going to Wellington was, of course, my pursuit of the kiwi and penguin eggs, for which I needed the permission of the New Zealand Division of Wild Life.

When I presented myself to the Wild Life Division, I was greeted with typical New Zealand friendliness; but the question of providing me with a kiwi egg was answered by a polite but positive refusal. One egg equals one kiwi and kiwis are disappearing. The kiwi is found in no place on earth but New Zealand, and the government **33** has enacted very rigid protective laws. That country has already lost the largest living bird of modern times, the moa, and protection of the kiwi is accepted by the New Zealanders almost as dogma.

Scientifically the kiwi is of great interest because it is classified, along with the ostrich, rhea, emu, and cassowary, as an "ancient bird."

The Wild Life Division suggested that I see Dr. Robert A. Falla, Director of the Dominion Museum. Dr. Falla had been the assistant zoologist with the 1929–1931 British–Australian–New Zealand Antarctic expeditions under Sir Douglas Mawson. After that, he had made several trips to Antarctica on HMNZS *Endeavor*. He was avidly interested in Antarctic activities and questioned me at length about my programs. His enthusiasm, as with most Antarcticans, carried him away, and we talked about the work we had both been doing, he in the past and I in the present.

I was not greatly surprised when Dr. Falla agreed to support my request for the kiwi egg. Because of his influence, I felt that I had, at last, a pretty good chance of getting the egg. It still had to be approved, however, by the New Zealand Division of Wild Life—the people who had already turned me down! I stopped there before I left for Australia, and the officials agreed to weigh Dr. Falla's recommendation and to let me know. I doubted that I could have the good luck to get permission on my first try. I knew I would return to New Zealand in a few days, so I continued on to Australia in hot pursuit of emu blood.

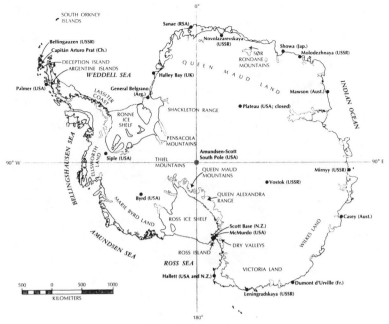

Map of Antarctica.

Ross Island and McMurdo Sound.

Air Force Hercules on ice at Williams Field
after flight from New Zealand.

McMurdo Base in 1966, with biolaboratory at center.

McMurdo Base, 1971, with Hut Point in foreground, Williams Field in background.

Author "lecturing" in biolaboratory at McMurdo.

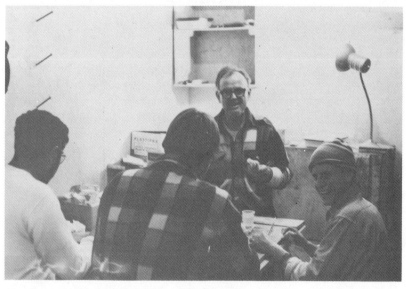

Bleeding and disecting fishing. Author (facing camera), Gus Trejo-Gonzalez
(left), Jim Norris (right), and Jim Moore (back to camera).

Author on first helicopter trip to Cape Crozier, 1964.

Edge of glacier that flows off Mount Erebus into McMurdo Sound.

7
Australia

My first stop at Canberra, Australia's capital, was at the American Embassy to try to enlist the help of our scientific attaché, Dr. Paul A. Siple. Meeting Dr. Siple was one of the great events of my life, for he was one of the finest men I have ever known.

When Siple was twenty years old, he was chosen, after tests among 600,000 Boy Scouts, to accompany Admiral Byrd on his first Antarctic expedition in 1928. He returned again and again to the Antarctic, headed the biology department of Byrd's 1933–1935 expeditions, and was the geographer for the U.S. expeditions in 1939 –1941. He was the original scientific leader of the first South Pole Station in 1956 and 1957. Dr. Siple's life *was* Antarctica, as one can sense by reading his fascinating book, *90° South*. It was a great blow to all Antarctic workers when he died suddenly of a stroke in 1969.

It was typical of Siple, although disappointing to me, that our conversation consisted of his asking and my answering questions about the current Antarctic programs. He was intensely interested in everything being done there, and he probed me with question after question about my own work. I wish I could have turned the conversation to him and his own accomplishments, but he wasn't that sort of person.

41

Dr. Siple, dedicated scientist that he was, agreed to help me obtain some emu blood and steered me to Sir Macfarlane Burnet at the Walter and Eliza Hall Institute for Medical Research at Melbourne. Burnet invited me to tea; while we were discussing Antarctic biology and biochemistry, his secretary came in with a telegram from Siple, telling me that New Zealand had agreed to provide me with a kiwi egg. The telegram also pointed out that the New Zealanders were aware that I was attempting to delineate possible biochemical relationships between the New Zealand penguins, the kiwi, and the Australian penguin. This bit of added information apparently turned the trick. Burnet was so impressed that anyone could get a kiwi egg from New Zealand—it had never been done before—that he immediately telephoned the right man, whoever he might have been. Before I knew what was happening, I was happily centrifuging emu blood in the biochemistry laboratory at the University of Melbourne. Happiness comes in strange forms to biochemists.

Before I left, the Australians helped me again. Their Antarctic Research Division made it possible to obtain egg whites of the royal penguin at Macquarie Island, a small island about halfway between Australia and Antarctica. I was certainly coming home with more than I expected. My only disappointment was my inability to obtain eggs of the rare Australian monotremes: the duckbill platypus and the echidna. I suppose, though, that if I had managed to get those, my list would have extended to other species, so I was far more grateful than disappointed when I returned to New Zealand for the last leg of my trip home.

I revisited Australia only once again, unfortunately, but I have made many stops at New Zealand during my repeated visits to Antarctica. It is always with a feeling of homecoming that I return to Christchurch, a feeling intensified by visiting my New Zealand friends, many of whom have also worked in Antarctica.

After my departure from New Zealand, friends there

continued my work by collecting and preparing eggs from three species of New Zealand penguins. They also helped two of my students who went there later to obtain blood serum from the New Zealand penguins. They have been most gracious, and I shall always be indebted to them.

My trip back to California was uneventful. My family, waiting at the airport, had worried about how I would hold up physically, but I came striding off the plane, sunburned and erect, with even a little gallop in my walk.

I soon settled back into the routine of laboratory work with my colleague, David T. Osuga. But laboratory work seemed to reach a higher pitch. I knew, while putting penguin egg whites through batteries of tests, that if it was at all possible I would return to Antarctica. And the next time, my research would be on a larger scale than I had been able to perform alone.

8
The Hostile Land

That winter I spent every spare hour satisfying my curiosity about Antarctica and its history.

I found that the names of the geographical features of the area are a roster of the early explorers. Captain James Cook tried to find the continent in 1772 but was unable to penetrate the ice barriers that encircled it. An American seal hunter, Captain Nathaniel B. Palmer, and a Russian admiral, Baron Fabian Gottlieb von Bellinghausen, both claimed to have sighted land in 1820. Later a Britisher spotted the same land and named it for Sir James Robert George Graham, who was then First Lord of the Admiralty, at about the same time that some Chileans saw it and named it for their hero, Bernardo O'-Higgins. The land they all saw was officially named in the early 1960s the Antarctic Peninsula.

Although the confusion over names was resolved sensibly by an international commission, the argument has not been forgotten. Once when in Australia, I inadvertently referred to Palmer Land and an Australian said, "Won't you American blokes realize that Graham Land is now called the Antarctic Peninsula?"

Others important in the early history of Antarctica included American Captain Charles Wilkes, who mapped more than 1500 miles of its coastline; Jules Sebastian

Cesar Dumont d'Urville, who tried unsuccessfully to find the South Magnetic Pole on commission from the French; Adrien de Gerlach of Belgium, who had to winter over because his ship became stuck in the ice; Captain Leonard Kristensen of Norway; Carsten E. Borchgrevink, a Norwegian under the British flag; and James Clark Ross, who named Victoria Land, Cape Crozier, Mounts Erebus and Terror (after the two ships of his expedition), and McMurdo Sound (after the first officer of the *Erebus*, Archibald MacMurdo).

All these men contributed importantly to the world's knowledge of Antarctica, but the three giants of its history before the age of aircraft and motorized equipment were Scott, Amundsen, and Shackleton, who explored the continent in the early twentieth century and who suffered unimaginable hardships.

Antarctica has been explored only recently, but it remains difficult to understand how so much of the world's population is so ignorant about such a large part of the world. Before my first trip to the ice in 1964, I was as green as anyone could be. My meager knowledge of Antarctica stemmed from being in New Guinea in World War II and the consequent development of a general interest in the Southern Hemisphere.

Antarctica is a mountainous land surrounded, except at the point between the tip of South America and the Antarctic Peninsula, by a thousand miles of water. The Arctic is a body of water surrounded by land; animals in the north polar region can migrate by land to warmer climates. But Antarctic animals must either swim or remain in an impossibly cold winter climate, so there are no polar bears, elk, or reindeer, only marine animals and birds among the vertebrates.

Fossils of tropical animals and plants found in Antarctica indicate that, in prehistory, it was part of a large tropical continent called Gondwanaland, which split up and drifted to form all the present-day southern continents. The splitting of the original continent must have **45** started about two hundred million years ago, and the Antarctic has been cold a long time. Continental drift is still taking place; Antarctica, for example, moves about two centimeters a year.

Animal and plant life in Antarctica must endure a difficult and rigorous environment. Over 95 percent of the continent is buried under ice averaging half a mile in depth. Most of the continent is below sea level, pushed down by the sheer weight of the ice. The small clear areas do not encourage life of any kind, for temperatures often drop well below minus 60°F in winter. Only two flowering plants have been found, and those only on the warmer northern tip of the Peninsula. The few lichens, mosses, fungi, insects, and unicellular forms that exist are primarily on the periphery of the continent, where oceanic birds enrich the soil.

Unlike the land, the oceans are teeming with life. Nearly forty species of sea birds have been found below the Antarctic Convergence (the meeting place of temperate and cold ocean waters, which is usually considered the border of the Antarctic); there are six species of seals and more than a dozen species of whales. Many fish, most of them found nowhere but in the Antarctic, live there, too. Besides vertebrates, there are zooplankton, phytoplankton, algae, crustaceans, sponges, echinoderms, sea spiders, nemertine worms, jellyfish, mollusks, and squids.

But how do men survive?

So much research has been conducted on the requirements of Antarctic survival that, except in cases of carelessness, the risks of personal disaster are slight. The instruction sheets issued to all arrivals at McMurdo are an indication of the care that must be taken in daily life. Instructions about protective clothing and personal hygiene rules are precise. A partial list includes: remain dry and never chill; keep mittens tied to the person; always wear sun-glasses when outdoors; and never leave camp alone. Rules also warn repeatedly of the dangers of fire.

9
A Dual Program

The 1965 season found me highly enthusiastic about returning to the ice. Our findings in the penguin studies, particularly of the egg whites, provided a powerful stimulus. Our Antarctic program was growing in enthusiasm and personnel. There was far more to discover than could be accomplished by myself on a spur-of-the-moment journey to accept the hospitality of Bob Wood and Bill Emison at Cape Crozier. The National Science Foundation agreed to help equip the laboratory at McMurdo with items necessary for our particular research.

Most of the arrangements were completed at the 1965 Skyland Planning Conference. There was time that year to meet many of the NSF officials, and two of them were to be directly involved with my ensuing work over several years' time. Dr. George Llano, head of the biology programs, was a noted botanist specializing in lichens. He had spent many months in Antarctica, and many times his advice and suggestions proved valuable to our programs. Kenneth Moulton, part of the logistics and operational arm, was the NSF representative at McMurdo for the coming year's work, as well as for several future years. His cool temperament helped in conquering the many unexpected problems that developed in Antarctica.

I realized that if I were to spend two months in that **47** violent climate, I would have to accept more rigorous physical challenges for a much longer time than I had the previous year. I worked out a plan of physical fitness that I followed carefully and still adhere to. My diet and habits were reasonable and sensible. I swam nearly every day, rode a bicycle regularly, and did special exercises on a specific schedule. I decided, next, to use any physical crutches available; in particular, I planned to use all the protective devices supplied by NSF and to wear my own back support. I decided, too, to make sure I stayed in good condition while I was on the ice. Finally, I planned to carefully avoid injury during the first few weeks on the ice, particularly, to make certain that the program would get under way. I wanted, besides, to give myself a little time to toughen up!

I selected my associates with great care. I was lucky to have two excellent colleagues in my research laboratory, and both were anxious to work on our program in Antarctica. Dr. Herman T. Miller, a postdoctoral fellow, had come to me from the Biochemistry Department of the University of Missouri Medical School at Columbia, and Richard G. Allison was a graduate student working with me toward his Ph.D. degree, which he later earned for his work on penguin blood-serum and egg-white proteins. Both men had the even temperament and dedication to research so necessary to work efficiently under Antarctic conditions.

Our primary objective was to obtain a large number of very fresh Adélie penguin eggs, which were needed to study the use of Adélie penguin egg-white proteins for long-range studies. Absolutely fresh eggs were essential for reliable research, since the analyses over a long period of time are used as a baseline for comparison of egg-white protein of other penguin species. Protein changes occur after the egg has been laid, and especially after incubation. Frozen eggs could be used for some of our tests, but we had to examine fresh eggs to know what **48** changes were due to freezing or to age.

We asked the National Science Foundation for permission to pick up a thousand eggs from the Cape Crozier rookery. They were astounded! The rookery produced about 300,000 eggs a year, and we wanted one out of every three hundred! Many ecologists, including some who are now my very good friends, thought this would be a major disaster. We pointed out that some estimates indicated that only 10 percent of all the eggs actually develop into mature egg-laying adults, so we were really only taking 100 birds. The arguments against our proposal were heated. The reviewing boards were understanding, fortunately, and granted us a permit to take 900 eggs. We had made our original estimate somewhat higher than our actual needs to allow for breakage in transport, but as it worked out, we took only 700 eggs after all.

One important limit was placed on our activities: we could take only the second egg of a normal two-egg clutch. After the female lays her first egg, she normally stays to lay the second one, then goes to sea to feed. If we took the first egg, she might leave without laying the second, and we would be responsible for the loss of two eggs per pair rather than one. The condition was a fair one, but it caused us much more labor than otherwise would have been required.

My attitude toward the preservation of wildlife has always been positive, but for the first time I had to grapple with the practicalities of how to preserve wildlife and still accomplish the work I had set out to do. Now, after a few more years of watching penguins in Antarctica, I can appreciate the opposition of my ecologist friends to our nest-robbing, even though its effects were minor. I agree that ecologists have right on their side in matters pertaining to conservation, but sometimes it must also be recognized that the needs of scientific research are valid.

The prime research target on the 1965 trip was to determine, as precisely as possible, the functioning of **49** proteins in the eggs, blood, and muscle tissues. To arrive at any findings peculiar to penguins, it was necessary to compare these findings with proteins of other birds; hence we wanted to collect and analyze the proteins of other species as well.

Our interest in eggs in general was in two related directions. One dealt with the eggs as a biological system, particularly as a place where the living creature develops. The other was the use of the eggs as sources of interesting biological materials, particularly proteins.

We had found that the egg proteins of two possibly distantly related water birds, shearwaters and gulls, were significantly different from the egg proteins of most other birds. Antarctic penguin eggs, we were convinced, should be still more different; penguins had been isolated from other related species for a long, long time, and there were probable effects of the laying and incubation of eggs in extreme cold.

Until our first trip to Antarctica, there had been very few biochemical studies done on penguins. Our biochemical approach would allow us to look at penguins at the level of their molecules, and by using biochemical agents and analysis, we could see what their molecules were like and how they functioned. This would provide valuable information about penguins and their evolutionary relationships with other birds. We hoped to get a "fingerprint" which might help us to understand how the biochemical systems work in other living things, since biochemical studies frequently reveal characteristics that are not apparent in visual or other physical studies.

Our work with penguin blood-serum and egg-white proteins would be expanded to include the biochemical taxonomy (classification) and evolution of the penguins. This required obtaining blood from individual penguins and injecting others to help us identify antibodies in the blood-serum and egg-white proteins. Our research with penguins turned out to be far more complicated than we had originally planned.

50

About this time hasty observations of the laboratory at McMurdo and what had been done there the previous year were beginning to pique my scientific curiosity. Here was the biggest ice cube in the world, the Ross Ice Shelf, stretching for hundreds of miles, helping to keep the ocean water at a constant temperature, and covering over, perhaps, the answers to thousands of biochemical mysteries.

One little-known project was particularly interesting. Cold-adapted fishes, snatched from the icy waters with special apparatus, were examined in a biological laboratory in an effort to discover how it was possible for life to be maintained in nearly freezing temperatures.

The leader of this project, Donald E. Wohlschlag, was the man who had called me the previous year to ask me about going to Antarctica. Dr. Wohlschlag was, at this time, preparing to leave the Antarctic program to direct the Institute of Oceanography at the University of Texas. His departure would leave a place for another senior researcher in his program. After serious reflection, I decided that our team would examine fishes in the same way we had examined penguins.

The obvious fields of investigation, in our view, were studies of muscle enzymes and blood-serum proteins. Upon our return to Skyland, we planned our techniques and obtained equipment to do the new work, for it was a logical extension of the research we had been doing on penguins. The National Science Foundation approved. When we returned to Antarctica, it was with two research programs instead of one.

Late in October, 1965, I again found myself in New Zealand, preparing for my second visit to the ice.

The trip from Christchurch to Williams Field was far easier than before; less cargo was aboard the plane, with less crowded conditions prevailing. The "point of no return" was now, I found, referred to as the "point of clearance for Williams Field." The semantic change was comforting. I also knew, this time, what to expect at the **51** end of the flight. As we flew over Cape Adare and along the mountain ranges on the edge of the Ross Sea, I could actually see where I believe Ross, Scott, and Shackleton had been.

Again we were fortunate to arrive on a clear, cold morning; we were assigned accommodations rapidly and had unpacked our equipment by mid-afternoon. Within two days, our laboratory had been set up, and we were ready for our big egg hunt at Cape Crozier and our fishing expedition at McMurdo.

10
Nest Robbing

I made a preliminary trip to Cape Crozier with Ken Moulton, the USARP representative, to select the area where we might take our eggs. We met two eminent ornithologists, Dr. William J. L. Sladen and Roger Tory Peterson, the well-known writer and editor of many books about birds. These men, plus two others who were away at the time, made up an ecological research team from Johns Hopkins University. We decided to take our eggs from an area of the rookery in which Sladen's group had made no studies. In fact, we left a buffer zone of thousands of penguins between us and the area where Sladen's group was working.

Our site was on a high slope, which would make our egg gathering difficult; but it was a compact area and only about half a mile from the Jamesway hut. Once the collecting started, the work would have to go on regardless of the weather, so we were pleased to be fairly close to our living quarters.

We also decided that Dick Allison should work with Sladen for about a week, and in return for his aid, Sladen would teach him how to number the colonies and help him map the area.

I returned to McMurdo with the feeling that the 900 eggs were really in the basket. I sent Allison to Dr. Sladen and turned my thoughts to fishing.

At McMurdo, the boys were already at work in the fishing house with Arthur L. DeVries, one of Dr. Wohlschlag's students, who was completing a year of wintering over, and some USARP volunteers who were awaiting transportation home. DeVries taught us the techniques of Antarctic fishing.

Our first catches were "borches" (*Trematomus borchgrevinki*), which came to the surface of the water in the hole we had cut in the ice before erecting our fishing house. The borches were from six to ten inches long and silvery like trout, although a dedicated trout fisherman would probably not consider them as pretty.

We baited drop lines with small pieces of seal meat and could see the borches rise up in the hole. They didn't bite very well on still bait, but a slight movement of the line would usually do the trick.

My introduction to fishing was cut short. A few days after Dick Allison left for Crozier, an emergency radio message one Sunday morning advised me that the penguins were "laying like mad." Coincidentally, we had seen large numbers of borches in the fish hole the day before. It might be all over in the next ten or twenty days as far as the fish were concerned, but we knew it would be all over in just a few days for the penguins. When things happen in Antarctica, they happen fast. Within an hour I was on my way back to Crozier; two hours later I was climbing over the rookery helping Dick collect eggs.

The change I saw in the activity of the birds was dramatic. Only eight days before I had seen many unoccupied nests, with Adélies waddling around collecting rocks to build new nests. Over 90 percent of the nests were now occupied by pairs of birds. A penguin was on each nest, and there was a great deal of commotion as the birds communicated with each other, both vocally and physically. Dick showed me his log book, which listed the number of nests he had to check and the number of birds he had to dislodge to do so. It was a tremendous task. He had barely managed to complete his rounds the day before; if I hadn't come immediately, our egg program would have been seriously curtailed.

We had planned to survey about twenty colonies, with an average of 100 nests per colony. This meant 4,000 birds at 2,000 nests, and possibly 4,000 eggs that had to be handled. We were to take the second egg from each normal two-egg clutch until we had reached our target. Taking the second egg, rather than the first, greatly increased the amount of labor required, since we had to remove each bird many times.

Dr. Sladen and Dr. Llano of the National Science Foundation had convinced us that we should include observations on egg-laying habits as a contribution to ecological knowledge. We kept records of the dates the penguins laid their eggs as we watched the colonies. We did the same in following years to see if our presence there created any disturbing effect. This work put our egg-snatching efforts in a different light; although it meant a lot more work, it helped me to come still closer to seeing things as an ecologist does. At least I was working with living creatures—not the usual role of a structural biochemist. But the job ahead looked a lot more formidable than I had foreseen. How could we safely and efficiently handle the research with fish at McMurdo in addition to the big penguin project here?

Each one of the 2,000 nests had to be looked at every day. When the first egg appeared, we dated it with a large felt-tipped pen. Each nest was then inspected twice a day for the next ten days. When the second egg was laid, we would take it and note the number of days elapsing between arrivals. Thus we had to pick up and look at all the eggs every day.

The hardest part was getting the penguins off their rocky nests. Sometimes, as we approached, the female would hop off the nest and the male would get on, apparently to protect it better, though both were quick to attack at our encroachment.

More often than not, the operation required dis- **55**

lodging both birds; when we had removed one penguin, the other would hasten to take its place. Thus, for each nest, we frequently had to lift eight to ten pounds of fighting, writhing, muscular penguins up to four times. Since most of the nests were not more than about three feet apart, six or eight birds in adjacent nests would join the attack against these huge egg-stealing predators. I know how a skua must feel! Sometimes four birds would attack from four different directions simultaneously, which meant fighting off 40 or 50 pounds of angry muscle exerting its force through snapping beaks and beating flippers.

In one respect, the proximity of nests to one another made the inspection easier, since we didn't have to walk very far between nests. On the other hand, it was a painful operation! One's rump, when he was bent over working at a particular nest, became an inviting target to the bird in the adjacent nest—a target he almost always took advantage of. It wasn't easy, while this was going on, to get out a pen, mark an egg, and make notes for the records we were assembling.

The job was tough enough when the weather was good. In foul weather it was almost impossible. Somehow, though, we did it.

Bad weather caused frequent falls. Leaning into the wind to keep his balance, even a strong man can be knocked over by a sudden gust of wind, most often into a mass of penguins and penguin dung.

Half way through the two-week period we were engaged in egg collecting, I caught a cold. (Legend has it that if one gets a cold during his first two weeks or so in Antarctica, he'll never have another one.) Because of the intense cold and wind, my nose ran profusely. My handkerchief was a roll of bathroom tissue I carried with me at all times. I used a roll a day. Blowing my nose required that I remove my gloves and sun glasses, since the nose-blowing process caused warm air to form ice on the inside of my glasses. The three days I had the cold, when I had to fight angry penguins, collect eggs, and make notes in howling snow, were probably the hardest days of my life.

I believe I took a hundred tumbles during the two weeks we collected eggs. Only one caused enough injury for a few days of lameness, though I suffered many bruises and scratches. When starting to fall, I would put my gloves over my face and, in my red Santa Claus outfit, just roll on down the rocks and penguin dung. I was well padded, which made the bumps and penguin whacks and pecks a great deal easier to bear.

The most annoying part of the work, at first, was being continually covered with penguin dung. After a while, though, I didn't notice the smell at all, because I smelled just like the penguins. We became one great big happy smelly family.

Gathering eggs was not always as arduous and hazardous as I have described it; we became more efficient with practice. We became adept at protecting our eyes from flippers and beaks. We learned to move at a certain speed and to avoid lifting our arms or our legs in ways that would startle or frighten the penguins. We learned to be quick in taking and returning the eggs to the nests. The work eventually became second nature to us, and even in our bright red coats, we soon blended almost naturally into the penguin colonies.

It would have been easier if we could have gathered eggs only during calm weather, for penguins are more calm when not under the stresses of high winds and white-outs. On bad-weather days, men and penguins were equally upset. Most of our memories, understandably, are of stormy weather, though our photographs and films were almost always made during days of calmness.

11
Snug Harbor

We had not quite collected our quota of eggs when the storm hit. For two days we had fought heavy winds and gusts and had expended so much energy that fatigue caused many more than the usual number of accidents. On the last day before the storm, we barely managed to complete the day's collection. That night the wind rose rapidly, an omen of another fierce Antarctic storm.

Four of us were safely in the Jamesway hut—Bill Sladen, Dick Allison, Roger Tory Peterson, and me—but we worried about John Boyd and Geoff Harrow of the Johns Hopkins party, who were about three miles away by the Ross Ice Shelf at the emperor rookery.

They had for protection only a small box-like emergency shelter; it was no place to be stranded in a fierce storm, so they made the decision to undertake the hazardous journey to our hut. The advisability of the trek was debatable, for a rapidly worsening storm might have made survival more likely in their shelter than enroute to our hut. In stormy weather travel between the two sites took three or four hours, provided they traversed a glacier or several hazardous cliffs at the edge of the ocean— much longer by a safer route. But the severity of the storm denied the safety of the longer route.

58   Radio communication, usually available between the shelter and the hut, was lost in the roar of rapidly deteriorating weather. As we in the hut set about making our own place secure, we prayed that Boyd and Harrow would choose the relative safety of their small shelter. It was a long evening. Late that night a pounding on the door signaled that they had safely accomplished the hazardous trek despite a bad case of frostbite suffered by John Boyd.

When the new arrivals had thawed out and John's frostbite had been treated, spirits livened because of the delightful personalities of these two men. John Boyd, son of a physician and biologist, was a good Antarctican who loved the outdoors and welcomed hard work. He treated difficulties with disdain and good humor. Geoff Harrow was from Christchurch and a fine example of a New Zealander. He donated his time without pay and was spending his vacation in Antarctica for the sheer love of it, rather than for money or scientific recognition. He was an expert mountain climber, a bird watcher, and a member of an official New Zealand mountain-rescue group. In Antarctica he advised in matters concerning icy areas and how to cross them. It was undoubtedly Geoff's skill that enabled him and John Boyd to reach the hut from the emperor rookery.

There were now six of us in the Jamesway hut. We were crowded, but as commonly happens in Antarctica, discomfort seemed to breed good nature. Bill Sladen and Roger Tory Peterson had both traveled the world studying birds. They could both imitate bird calls and chatted back and forth with whistles and cheeps. It would have made a great recording!

We took turns cooking, and some of the results were spectacular. Our first meal was at 8 A.M., the time of our radio contact with McMurdo. The other meal was after work, around six or seven in the evening. At noon, everyone scrounged for himself.

Breakfast was hearty. The menu varied from scrambled eggs or omelettes with cheese or onion to sausages, **59** pancakes, and perhaps tidbits from the previous evening's meal. It was nearly always preceded by oatmeal and some kind of canned fruit.

During the egg-gathering period, we frequently made omelettes from fresh penguin eggs that had been cracked or kicked from the nest and frozen. Penguin-egg omelettes need a little more milk than omelettes made of chicken eggs. They are fishy tasting but not objectionably so. Boiled or fried penguin eggs are tasty enough but are exasperating to cook because the whites and yolks coagulate at different rates; the whites remain translucent and unappetizingly glassy when cooked.

Obtaining the ingredients for scrambled chicken eggs was a fatiguing task. Because the eggs came to us frozen in 30-pound tin buckets, the cook required a screwdriver and hammer to knock out a chunk of frozen egg from the can.

Preparing dinner became a competitive sport which taxed the ingenuity and imagination of each cook. Meat was always the entree, and we had plenty of it. Large stocks of frozen prime steaks, pork chops, beef hamburger, chicken parts, and canned ham were on hand, and we had dried condiments and additives to make exotic curries, sauces, and gravies—exotic by our standards, at any rate.

"Hoosh," according to the dictionary, is a kind of thick soup. I developed a special sort of hoosh that was praised, or at least eaten, by my colleagues.

For a group of six, I took eight pounds of prime steak and cut it into three-inch squares an inch thick. I seared them in the bottom of a pan and added a quarter of a cup of vinegar and enough water to cover the meat about an inch. I would add about a tablespoon of salt and a little garlic salt, cover the pan, and place the mixture on the heating stove (not the cooking stove). The starting temperature was about 50°F. Apparently the warming process was slow enough that the temperature range remained where the enzymes of the meat were highly active for several hours. When I removed the mixture, after about six hours, the water was just hot to the touch. I would then add a half pint of Scotch or bourbon and perhaps a little more water to make up for evaporation. I would put it back on the heater and two hours later add another half pint or less of whiskey—it depended on my mood. I would now add other embellishments to provide character; these would change from time to time. Sometimes embellishment meant a couple of canned boiled potatoes, dehydrated onions, peppers, string beans, or other vegetables. On other occasions, I added a can or two of mushroom, cream of pea, or other condensed soup, whatever my whim at the time. The mixture was then placed on the Coleman cooking stove and simmered (at about 190°F) for about 15 minutes.

My hoosh could be served in two ways: as a stew with the large hunks of meat still relatively intact, or with the stock used as a sauce or gravy. I'd probably not serve my hoosh as a daily dish in my own home, being a rather infrequent user of alcoholic beverages, but it tasted great after a cold day's work. Leftovers were supplemented by cans of stew or beans the following night.

My culinary expertise was certainly equalled, if not excelled, by my colleagues. I never understood the techniques Bill Sladen used, but he seemed able to mix almost any collection of ingredients and produce a gastronomic delight.

A warming beverage we sometimes made at Cape Crozier after a particularly cold day in the field was "Cape Crozier Hot Chocolate Scotch." It isn't difficult to make if you have hot chocolate at the ready; simply add a generous slug of Scotch to a cup of hot chocolate. It is guaranteed to put one to sleep as soon as he zips up his sleeping bag!

The consumption of alcoholic drinks is quite low at Cape Crozier. We never drank before work or if the weather was dangerous. Almost without exception, drinkers, even the "social" types, are not welcome in Antarctic **61** field work. A glove carelessly left on the stove by a befuddled man before retiring might start a fire that would be fatal to us all.

At Hallett Station, another penguin colony on the continent, good hard liquor is available in apparently unlimited amounts at tax-free prices of $2 or less a fifth. But the rule at Hallett the year I was there was that any man caught drunk and incapable of performing his duties lost his right to purchase liquor. A strong deterrent, though it didn't always work.

Two or three days after the arrival of Boyd and Harrow, the storm had broken enough for us to resume our field activities. But the weather was still too bad for transportation by helicopter, for which we had to wait another five days.

Dick and I used the extra time helping the Johns Hopkins group check wing bands on penguins at the edge of the ocean. Part of their work was recording and studying the dates birds would leave their rookery to go to sea to eat, and the dates they returned.

The few extra days that we stayed at Cape Crozier were memorable. But perhaps that is an understatement.

12
Crises

During the few days we were by the sea making our reports for Bill Sladen, we saw large numbers of leopard seals chasing penguins in the ocean. Numerous trails along the edge of the ice were made by the penguins trooping back and forth in long lines, awaiting the opportunity to dive in without danger from the seals, which swim back and forth under the edge of the ice ready to pounce.

I had a pocket movie camera with me that year and wanted to get a closeup of a leopard seal catching a penguin. I thought I might get a good shot if I walked along the penguin trails, many of which are only a foot wide, right at the edge of the ice, slippery, and sloping toward the ocean. I didn't think about it, really, but one slip could have sent me tumbling into the water, perhaps to face the evil fangs of a hungry leopard seal. The top of the ice edge is only three or four feet above water level, and the temperature of the water is almost freezing. In some places, the seas have eroded the ice, forming a shelf over the water. Once he had fallen in, a man wearing heavy Antarctic gear would find it impossible to throw himself back onto the ice. Even if he survived the frigid water, a prowling leopard seal would find him easy prey.

I spotted a leopard seal chasing a single penguin **63**

and, disregarding the precarious footing, took off for a spot about 50 yards down the edge of the ice where I knew penguins frequently shot up out of the water to land on the ice. I figured this would be the place of safety the penguin would seek.

I had reached a point only a foot from the edge of the ice, when I heard a loud bang just behind me and was simultaneously sprayed with sea water. Turning around to see what made this shotgun-like sound, I found myself staring eyeball-to-eyeball at a thousand-pound leopard seal!

The seal had lunged out of the water, half his upper body over the ice edge near me. Startled, I fell backwards and rolled toward the edge, managing to brace myself with my feet only inches from disaster. Just inches away, too, large sharp teeth menaced in gaping jaws!

The seal thought, perhaps, that the sound of my scraping feet was made by nearby penguins. More likely he considered penguin a greater delicacy than this unfamiliar red-coated animal. For whatever reason, he turned quickly and, clamping his fangs into a hapless penguin at the edge of the ice, slid into the water and disappeared. He was probably incapable of throwing himself completely up out of the water, but he certainly managed to get half way there and to hang on long enough to look me over at close range.

I lay on the ice for what seemed a long time, shaking and frozen from fear instead of cold. Any movement might cause me to slide over the edge into the water, with the leopard seal somewhere down below. I started, finally, to inch my way away from the edge of the ice. After about ten minutes, still only a few feet away, I lay for a quarter of an hour perspiring from fear. When I stood up my legs wobbled, but I made sure that if I fell it would be away from the water.

Although my experiences were not unique, I wonder even today how I made it through my first year or two on the ice.

Dr. Richard Penney told me of a somewhat similar incident with a leopard seal, though I confess he acted in a manner more in keeping with what an Antarctican should do. Rich was at the edge of the ice making some observations in connection with his research when a leopard seal suddenly made a jump for him. Its jaws were extended, sharp teeth bared for a kill. Penney, a young, vigorous, outdoor biologist, didn't retreat. He stabbed at the beast with his sheath knife and it disappeared.

The beauty of the cape was breathtaking a few days later when, while taking observations near the edge of the ice, I decided to take a stroll by myself; I was only about a quarter mile from the hut but completely out of sight of my colleagues.

I decided that, by taking a small hike up the mountainside, I could get a superb view of a glacier tongue and could use my field glasses to observe penguins swimming out to sea. I had started about ten o'clock in the morning and was well on my way by eleven. Suddenly I was overwhelmed by an unworldly feeling of euphoria. I could see Mount Terror shining above me, and it seemed to be beckoning to me. The ocean shore was out of sight, but I could see the broken sea ice extending several miles into the ocean. The air was still, the sun bright, and I felt an eerie feeling of complete tranquillity. I was sure I could climb to eternity! I reasoned that it was only eleven o'clock, that the weather was as perfect as it could possibly be, and that I was equipped for a long hike. I had my heavy Antarctic mittens and mukluks on; I didn't usually wear mukluks when merely going to the water's edge because of their tendency to become heavy frozen masses of ice when hit by spray. I was carrying a generous bag of nuts, crackers, and cheese. I reasoned also that there is no night in the Antarctic at that time of year, and no fear of impending darkness. Why was I so well prepared for a long lonesome hike? I didn't know then, and I don't know still.

I knew only that I had to climb Mount Terror. It was **65**

a drive I neither tried nor wanted to shrug off. My mind reeled with complex problems of my position at the university, my family, my research. As I walked, these problems and hundreds of other thoughts came into sharp focus. I was walking into a Nirvana of beauty, peace, and composure. I reasoned that if I climbed for four or five hours, the descent would be a bit faster, and I could return in three or four.

The beckoning mountain won, and I was off on my trip. Three hours later, after a fall into a small crevasse, during which I lost one of my big mittens, I was engulfed suddenly by thoughts of friends and family. I was flooded with shame when I realized that I loved and was loved by these wonderful people. They depended on me, yet I had succumbed to a sort of mental intoxication, like a psychedelic trip. Still, I walked aimlessly for half an hour before I forced myself to quit and to return.

I got back to the hut at midnight, thirteen hours after I had left; I was too ashamed to tell my colleagues what had happened, and I can give no explanation even now.

The following morning we were told by radio that McMurdo's weather had cleared and that a helicopter would pick us up the next day, unless the weather again became unruly. Dick had been at Crozier for 24 days and I for 17, though we felt like homesteaders.

One of our last jobs before we left was to catch six penguins to take back to McMurdo for blood examinations. We selected two pairs and two unmated birds. We wanted pairs because the chances of eggs hatching and chicks growing were small if we took only one bird; chicks would need a second parent to search for food. It seemed less upsetting to take two pairs from two nests than four single birds from each of four separate nests. One of the two single birds was a young one, who might have been attempting to attract a mate for the first time. The other single bird was sorry and magnificent at the same time, a one-legged male who stood at the upper edge of one of the top colonies on the hillside rookery, his beak pointing toward the sky and his flippers beating in an ecstatic attempt to attract a mate. He had traveled over half a mile at a continual climb by taking tiny hops on his single leg. We should have left that forlorn but stately figure there, but common sense dictated that we take him. There was little chance that he would ever sire and raise chicks.

The following morning we put our six penguins in a pen that also housed four penguins being studied by Bill Sladen. Half an hour later all ten had escaped. Half the escapees were still nearby and were quickly caught, while four of the remaining five were merrily running down the hillside toward the rookery. The fifth, our one-legged hero, was hopping, falling, and rolling behind the others. An hour's search of the rookery turned up three of the missing five. We never found the last two, one from Bill Sladen's study and the other our one-legged friend. I like to think that the same courage and strength that helped him elude us also helped him attract a mate and become a proud father.

The helicopter came for Dick Allison and me about noon. The year before, at the same place, I had been met by a helicopter full of nice clean visitors coming out for a look at the rookery. This time the helicopter carried Marlin Perkins, well known to millions for his television programs about wildlife. He had come to our penguin city to take motion pictures of emperor penguins. Marlin and Roger Tory Peterson spent a busy afternoon grinding out shots at the emperor rookery. The main job for us scientists was keeping out of camera range!

We were back at McMurdo Base, a very different environment, in an hour and a half. We had inside plumbing, we could take a shower every week, watch movies every night (if we had wanted to), and eat regular Navy chow. And we had, of course, the frozen mud from vehicles continually plowing around McMurdo Base, moving cargo, snow for water, supplies, and fuel. **67**

I liked life at McMurdo, partly because we were out on the ice in our fishing house a good part of the time, but also because of the interesting people being outfitted for trips to the field.

I missed the freedom and isolation of Cape Crozier, but McMurdo had many advantages and enjoyments. One of these was an underwater observation chamber into which one could climb to watch marine life swimming by. Here, 25 feet below the surface of the ice, in a world of complete silence, just enough light came through the ice to let one see the many-colored marine forms that were all around.

The observation chamber offered nearly complete serenity but was not without its perils. Once, an overweight visitor became stuck in the entrance pipe; it took several men a long time to pry him loose. On another occasion, Navy officers found unexploded dynamite only 20 feet below the chamber while the Admiral in command of the base watched the sea life from inside. The incident created a great deal of consternation; naturally, I wondered if the dynamite had been there during some of my visits to the chamber.

We fished for another week and a half until my departure time arrived. Dick Allison and Herman Miller remained to carry on the work for another three weeks.

We all returned at different times on similar post–World War II Globemasters, piston-engine planes that had been "refurbished" by contract air-transport companies. On my flight from Christchurch to Travis, we stopped for engine repairs at three different places, each stop preceded by mid-ocean instrument failure. When Miller and Allison flew home, they arrived in Honolulu with only three functioning motors.

We got back to California in time for Christmas at home. Compared to the perils of the American highway, Antarctica seemed a pretty safe place after all.

13
Plans for Return

Soon after our return from the 1965 visit to the ice, we began making plans to return the following season. We pressed hard on our work with fish-blood and muscle samples to determine if we wanted to begin a fish-blood program as extensive as that we had undertaken with the penguins. We decided that we did.

We began preparing for a major assault against the problem of cold adaptation for the season beginning in October 1966. The work with fish enzymes would require different chemicals and equipment from what we had used in our egg work, although some of the biochemical procedures would be the same. We had to check the list of chemicals and equipment waiting for us at McMurdo Base and order the other items we would need while we were there.

We also had to pick our team. Dr. Miller had completed four years of postdoctoral work with us and was leaving for a post at Lincoln University; Dick Allison had a heavy work schedule to prepare for his Ph.D. qualifying examination. Luckily, I have never been short of applicants for Antarctic research work, and I have, in fact, had to turn down many highly qualified individuals.

My new team consisted of my associate, David T. Osuga, who had been working with me at Davis on the **69** penguin egg whites; Stanley K. Komatsu, a predoctoral student; and John C. Bigler, a premaster's student.

Dave Osuga had been with me for more than six years, having stayed on as a permanent associate after receiving his master's degree. He was an ocean and river salmon sports fisherman whose talents fit in nicely with our missions.

Stan Komatsu had received his bachelor's degree from the University of Hawaii and had been one of my graduate students for the preceding two years. The idea of combining biochemistry with fishing in Antarctica excited him.

John Bigler had decided to work on his master's degree with me because of his determination to go to Antarctica. One of his pastimes was amateur bird watching, which was most valuable in our work with penguins.

One of the wonderful things about scientific research is that something new, some previously unknown thing, has always to be uncovered. Work is carried on not only for the sake of making discoveries that will bring promotion and recognition by colleagues but for the joy of fulfilling one's curiousity and using one's creative imagination. A scientist is sometimes like a detective attempting to solve a crime, although the former can plan his attack in more imaginative ways. There is often much drudgery, of course, but it's work that is necessary to reach goals that may benefit mankind.

Antarctic fishes have a number of adaptive features making it possible for them to live in the cold. Some characteristics at the physiological and biochemical levels can be pinpointed as being directly connected with cold adaptation; others can be only loosely connected with it.

Fish, unlike marine mammals such as seals and whales, usually have no way of controlling their body temperatures. Their bodies and all their constituent tissues and fluids, therefore, assume the same temperature as the water. In studying molecular systems directly related to cold adaptation in our laboratory, we have been particularly interested in the fact that fish can function efficiently at a temperature of 28.7°F (-1.85°C) in an ice-salt water mixture. This icy temperature is not much lower than the temperature at which some trout live in the United States, but it is enough colder to make adaptation more complicated. One of the adaptations specifically involves enzymes and the mechanisms that cause blood to clot.

We were dealing primarily with borches (*Trematomus borchgrevinki*) and mawsoni (*Dissostichus mawsoni*). Both are classified as Antarctic cod. The borches are about 10 or 11 inches long and have large heads and mouths, as do most Antarctic fishes. The much larger mawsonis are four to six feet long and weigh between 40 and 200 pounds.

Other Antarctic fish also have unique characteristics. Early whalers brought back stories of bloodless fishes they had caught for food around South Georgia Island. Later, a scientist named Ruud made extensive studies of this family and found that all species he examined were lacking in red blood cells and were really white blooded.

Hemoglobin, the red protein that transports oxygen around the body of almost all species of animals, is completely missing in these fish, yet they have oxygen in their tissues. One explanation is that the solubility of gases in water is inversely proportional to the temperature, and since the fish live in water sometimes below freezing, the oxygen may simply be dissolved in the water of the blood. Our plan was to discover how this phenomenon occurs. Actually, we eventually became so deeply involved in other investigations that we never did study this particular problem; but we did study another protein in the blood serum called transferrin. (The name "transferrin" literally means "iron-carrying"; the transferrin supplies the iron to tissues and cells that need it.) We found that even in fish with no hemoglobin, a major recipient of the body's iron, the blood serum contained the same amount of transferrin as fish with hemoglobin.

71

We also found another fascinating substance present in the fish blood. Originally discovered by Professor Per Scholander, then of our sister campus at San Diego, it was later studied by Art DeVries at Stanford. Scholander and his coworkers observed that the blood of Arctic fish contained a unique substance that lowered its freezing temperature without creating an osmotic condition fatal to the fish. The substance is termed "antifreeze protein."

In our third year on the ice we collected blood serum for the purpose of learning more about this antifreeze glycoprotein, work that absorbed much of our energies and proved to be stimulating and productive.

The success of an Antarctic scientific program like ours depends, I found, on three essential factors:

First, individuals must be adequately prepared, physically, scientifically, and technologically. The National Science Foundation helped considerably by the orientation programs at Skyland each year, but the main tasks were in the hands of the project leaders. Men had to be carefully chosen and prepared for the work ahead. They needed a thorough knowledge of the science relevant to the research activities and full awareness of the conditions under which they would work. Preparations included studying methods, practicing them to the point of expertise, and developing the knowledge and judgment to take sensible shortcuts when necessary. They had to know also how to fabricate special items of laboratory equipment.

Second, the field programs and laboratory work at McMurdo had to be planned well in advance. This included scheduling different types of field work in the huts at the rookeries or in the fishing houses and the interlocking of these with laboratory tests and the processing of samples for shipment. Multiple and alternate activities also had to be planned. One of the difficulties was the necessity of continuing research when the weather was bad or when proper equipment and laboratory sup-

plies were not available. If a heavy storm broke or if some

supplies were not available, we learned to shift our plans and do something else. The ability to change plans and schedules gave much greater efficiency and helped morale. A good researcher is frustrated by circumstances beyond his control. We even resisted the temptation to try completing a problem the first year we started it. Usually, we planned survey work the first year and completion the second. Several times we had to finish work during yet a third year because we didn't have the proper materials or had encountered unexpected difficulties.

Third, the Antarctic programs had to be correlated with our work at Davis. The workers at McMurdo had to be aware of what the researchers at home, with their greater facilities and equipment, were finding. The exchange of information involved shipping samples and reagents to and from Antarctica either with individuals or by airmail in ice chests or dry-ice containers. The materials would be examined or tested quickly and the results transmitted by radio or airmail. Radio messages were often sent to Davis for a recheck of laboratory procedures. Information and special supplies had to be sent to Antarctica quickly to ensure that proper changes in techniques were made.

Just as important were the arrangements for the work in California. Over 90 percent of the work of our Antarctic program has been done in our laboratory at Davis. Careful planning to provide the workers in California with material of the highest quality was required. It would have done no good to have obtained blood, muscle, heart, or brain materials in Antarctica if work could not be completed because of inadequate testing when it was first gathered or because of deterioration during transit or storage.

These were some of the things we had to plan and watch for at all times. When we were again ready to go on the ice, we felt sure we had prepared for almost any eventuality, although we knew that a hundred unexpected things might happen and usually did.

Scooping ice from fishing hole after dynamiting. Author third from left.

Fishing house burning down, 1966.

Author (left) and Stan Komatu cutting up frozen seal
for fish bait, 1966.

Author outside fishing house, 1968.

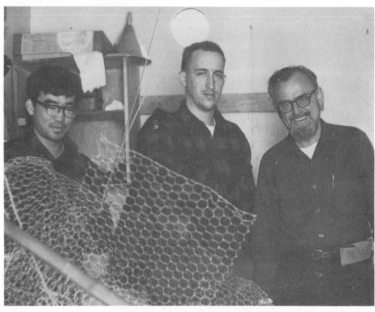

Opening fish trap, 1966. From left, Stan Komatsu,
John Bigler, and author.

Weddell seal rising in fishing hole inside house, 1968.

Dave Osuga displaying a *Dissostichus Mawsoni*, 1966.

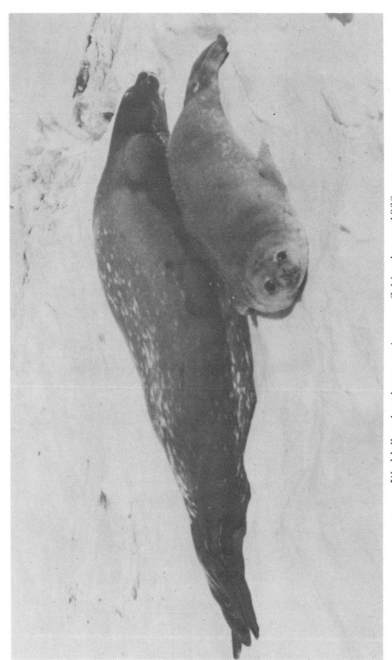

Weddell seal and pup on ice near fishing house, 1968.

Cape Crozier with Beaufort Island in the distance.

14
Men and Loneliness

Stan Komatsu desperately wanted the experience of wintering over, which meant staying in Antarctica for 14 months. It was with some reluctance that I discouraged him from spending the long black winter on the ice.

The physical and psychological problems didn't worry me much in Stan's case; he was in splendid physical, mental, and moral shape. My concerns were different, perhaps because I am a research scientist. Despite my confidence in Stan, my decision was based on the possibility of adverse effects on his educational program.

The effects of wintering over are usually much more than one might expect in an absence of several months from one's home or job. There are physical and psychological experiences that do not exist any place else on earth.

There is no transportation in or out of the Antarctic during the long winter, with the possible exception of a midwinter flight made in an emergency. The scientists were thus almost completely isolated. Further, it would be practically impossible to obtain the chemicals that might be needed as research changed or progressed. Except in the largest laboratories, most biochemists do not even attempt, because of cost and space, to stock many of the reagents they may need, relying instead on the airmail services of chemical-supply houses. Supplying chemicals to Antarctica in the winter would be out of the question.

The lack of ready access to books and reference journals is equally serious. I could, perhaps, have spent a sabbatical leave at Canterbury University at Christchurch and, from there, have had weekly discussions by radio with students wintering over on the ice. I could have used New Zealand library facilities to help make decisions as research progressed. But I couldn't be there in 1966. I had my work at Davis.

Another problem is being the only individual in a particular field wintering over. Two or even three people with similar interests on the ice during the winter can discuss mutual problems professionally and have the advantage of the others' suggestions and criticisms.

No, I didn't think Stan, at his age, was quite ready to try! The problems had often been extremely difficult even for older people.

I once encountered a Naval officer in Christchurch who had just returned from wintering over. We ate at the officer's mess together. Almost immediately he brought up the subject of the ineptness of USARP men. I thought it slightly indelicate, but he persisted in claiming that USARP representatives should have no status whatsoever because of their low competence. A look from another officer seemed to urge me to understand the fellow, but I challenged him anyway. I pointed out that I had had some experience in the Antarctic and that I was interested in making the system work. But I couldn't get through to him.

A week or two later I learned he had resumed his normal cooperative attitude toward scientists. His winter on the ice had resulted, apparently, in a temporary loss of the ability to judge merits and values.

I had also noticed that most of the scientists who wintered over showed little or no depth of creativity, although usually it redeveloped when the Antarctic stations were reopened in the spring. **81**

A biologist who had been at McMurdo prior to my first arrival summed it up by declaring that wintering over *appears* to be the answer to an intellectual's prayer. He expects to have the peace and the time to do all the things he's always wanted to do—writing the Great American Novel, perhaps, or solving a scientific problem that has been escaping solution. In fact, the very opposite occurs.

With uninterrupted time, a man can go down and stand at the edge of the ice and look across at its great expanse until the cold drives him back again. His mind is clear and tranquil—and empty! There are exceptions, certainly, but a pattern of noncreativity does seem to develop.

Loneliness brings up many other problems. I have often been asked about the existance of homosexuality and about the effect on men of living so long in a completely masculine society. I have no question that the absence of women causes a problem, a general one, but it is not the development of homosexuality so much as the onset of boredom.

Buddy relationships that develop are usually strong and long-lasting. Some appear to be like the love affairs of teenagers. Very few relationships approach anything at all resembling physical homosexuality, and I am sure that many of them become the basis for life-long friendships. The men joke about homosexuality. One of the jokes I heard soon upon arrival concerned a man wintering over, who had been there just a short time at the start of the wintering period. To a veteran of the previous year he confided, "Say, I've found a man who's a fairy. Do you think I'd better tell the captain?" The veteran promptly replied, "Hell no, let the captain find his own!"

Possibly as a carry-over from World War I, sex stories about the French are frequent. One concerns the French translation of the international rules for the protection of wildlife in Antarctica. Regulations state that penguins should in no way be disturbed. Retranslated into English, the French translation ended up as a stricture that the seaman should under no circumstances molest the penguins. Molestation of the penguins also crept into one of the tales about an earlier French expedition that wintered over near a colony of emperor penguins. According to this story, a French seaman and a 70-pound emperor penguin conducted a picturesque love affair during the long winter of isolation.

The men are pretty well instructed in the difficulties of being isolated for a long period. There is, of course, a healthy profusion of pinup pictures and dog-eared copies of *Playboy*, usually with the centerfold torn out, but I have never seen anything approaching the type of erotic magazines that are available in many stores in most big cities in the United States.

One of the big questions in my mind about the psychiatric studies of wintering over is, who studies the psychiatrists? If the conditions are such that almost everyone becomes a little disoriented, how about the man who is collecting the data?

Reports concerning personal hygiene are strange. Personal hygiene habits, both good and bad, may be indicative of the character and stability of the man, although under the strange circumstances of wintering over most ordinary rules of behavior are disregarded. One man, for example, never cleaned his room during an entire winter, despite vomiting all over it during an illness. Another man never took a bath for six months; he showed no anxiety, apparently slept well, and got along all right with his companions. One man ironed all his clothes after washing them—an unheard-of procedure—but never cleaned his room.

Some men have shown reasonable habits in personal hygiene, as judged by stateside standards, and become outrageously sloppy when they return to their normal home environment. One example is a man who never changed his shirt or shorts. His clothes were filthy and full of holes. After his comrades got after him, he slowly became more tidy and was almost "normal" when he left the ice. When he returned home he resumed his slovenly habits. The tidiness he acquired in antarctica was apparently, for him, an abnormal state.

One puzzlement is why there is more friction and personality clashes between the men near the end of the wintering over period. At the very end there is a sharp increase in difficulty. Irritations run high. One conclusion, a psychologist told me, is that the men know they are going to leave and may never again see these people with whom they have lived so closely. Thus they don't worry about controlling their tempers or inhibitions.

Three polar legends concern infectious diseases. One is that such diseases do not occur during the long wintering over isolation. This is only partly true. Apparently respiratory infections die out in an isolated group in Antarctica during the winter (May–September), probably because immunity is built up when only a small number of diseases are brought in by a small number of people.

Another legend is that a newcomer to Antarctica comes down with a respiratory infection within a few weeks after his arrival. There have in fact been some instances that seem to support this theory; of the three men in their thirties I took to Antarctica, all came down with respiratory infections. One was hospitalized for five days, another was immobilized for ten days, beginning about ten days after his arrival, and the third developed a debilitating cough after about two weeks. I do not know whether the younger graduate students experienced these same infections or not. There was no recurrence of the ailments I know about after the first incident.

Still another legend has it that men come down with respiratory infections when stored items, especially clothing, are taken out of storage. No data appear to support this theory, but some of the medics think it quite possible that stored clothing could introduce infectious agents or

84 even allergens into the environment.

The "ten-foot stare" is one of the characteristics that Antarcticans associate with wintering over. It's exactly what the name describes: a blank stare with the eyes focused on a space ten feet away.

The ten-foot stare is seen in a person sitting or standing, either by himself or in a crowd, or talking to someone else. The phenomenon gave me a squeamish feeling when I first encountered it. A man engaged in normal conversation will suddenly stop and, as if hypnotized, stare straight ahead as if transfixed by a spot in space. After a while he returns to normalcy and picks up the conversation as if nothing had happened. His friends and others who know about wintering over ignore it completely.

Few of these strange happenings are encountered by men who go to Antarctica for a few weeks or so during the austral summer. At Cape Crozier, for example, life is busy, never dull, and mostly creative. A professor's wife in California once remarked that I must have played a lot of cards while in Antarctica. In fact, I never even saw a deck of cards at Crozier.

These, then, were some of the reasons I used to persuade Stan Komatsu not to winter over. We planned on his only staying on the ice for five months, from October 1966 to February 1967.

Before we left the United States, we had worked out a schedule for our duties and studies in Antarctica. Stan, John Bigler, and I would go in early October, and I would be replaced by Dave Osuga shortly after December 1. John Bigler would come away in the middle of January so he could resume his classes at Davis, and Dave Osuga and Stan Komatsu would leave for home in February.

The schedule worked out perfectly. The weather cooperated perfectly to permit me to leave Antarctica just as Dave was going in. We even had our hoped-for meeting in Christchurch to swap notes and plan the oncoming work.

15
Through the Ice

Stan Komatsu, John Bigler, and I arrived at Williams Field about the middle of October. After exhuming our stored equipment and checking on the new material that had been sent down for the year, we planned our fishing house.

The location of the first hole is always a matter of conjecture, so I chose a spot where I knew Art DeVries had had some success the year before.

We were soon out on the ice, this time without Art's experience to lean on. We knew that fishing is fishing no matter where it is in the world or who the fishermen are. The tricks and techniques used in Antarctica are about the same as they are anywhere else, with some spectacular exceptions.

Most fish catches in Antarctica are made for scientific purposes by trawling. Research ships are equipped with devices that can operate near the surface or as much as half a mile deep. Deep-water fishing, as most sports fishermen do it, is rarely done in Antarctic waters. The weather is too cold and unpredictable.

Over the years we caught fish in five or six different ways, but in the beginning, we worked through the ice in fishing houses, using hook and line with bits of seal meat for bait. Sometimes we trapped through the ice, too.

The fishing houses were much the same as those used in northern North America for ice fishing, but Antarctic houses were larger. They varied from 15 to 20 feet long and from 8 to 12 feet wide. Heavy runners and a strong tongue made it possible to haul them across the ice by snow tractors. They were painted bright red so they could be seen easily. The ice hole, three to four feet in diameter, was at one end of the house. All our fishing houses were equipped with stoves like the ones in the Jamesway huts and with oceanographic winches for raising and lowering traps in deep water.

The hole was dug first, and the house then pulled over it. The ice was often as thick as 15 feet, and although we perfected various techniques of digging fish holes over the years, we never found an easy way! That first year, we cut the holes manually with chain saws and removed the blocks of ice with tongs. When the holes were deeper than eight feet, and they usually were, it was a long haul to pull a hundred-pound piece of ice to the top of the hole. (One of my rules was that anyone over fifty years old was not permitted to cut more than the first four feet. I was, of course, always the only one over fifty.)

After the cutting had gone as deep as possible, the bottom of the hole was blown out by dynamite. But we still weren't finished, for after dynamiting, the hole filled with ice and sea water, which we had to remove with tongs, screens, and picks. We sometimes hauled out more than a ton of ice at this stage. Finally, when the hole was clear, we would pull the house over the hole and bank the sides heavily with snow or chopped ice. We usually kept the fire going in the fishing house while digging so we could warm up and dry out. When we moved the house over the hole, we kept the fire going in the stove to prevent the hole from freezing over, as well as to keep us from freezing.

Both weather and luck governed how wet and cold we got during the digging. Often we were nearly covered with suits of ice frozen on our wet clothing by the cold wind. We usually wore rubber boots, but an unlucky fellow with water-filled boots had to make a quick change or risk frozen feet.

Another difficulty was that bad weather occasionally forced us to start digging before the house was ready.

Paul Dayton, a graduate biology student from the University of Washington, improved our method of cutting holes by suggesting that we remove less ice by sawing and tonging and more by dynamiting. But that was two years after our first attempts at cutting holes in the ice. An even greater refinement was made in 1969 when the Navy provided a huge drill that cut holes two feet in diameter. With this device we could drill a cluster of holes and dynamite both the walls between the holes and the bottom.

In 1966, though, we knew only what hearsay had told us about cutting holes in ice, and our efforts were almost disastrous.

Our fishing house had been moved close to where we planned to dig. We started attacking the ice with the chain saw, and we had made some progress when the weather changed for the worse. We agreed that we were "weathered in" and couldn't do much outside, so we began to fix up our house as a laboratory.

The fishing house wasn't really the Antarctic Hilton. Despite its bright red paint it was dirty and dilapidated inside, with the floor soaked with oil from long use. A shiny, new, empty fishing house nearby had been designated as a temporary storehouse for a few weeks, and though we tried to exchange houses, it was without success. We had many pretty names for the administrators and their clean unused fish houses.

For two days we watched the snow blow parallel to the ice. The wind was coursing the snow around our house and, when it finally subsided, we had to dig ourselves out. We moved the mountain of snow that had
88 gathered around our working area, dynamited the

bottom of our hole, pulled our house over it, and sealed it up with ice and snow. We congratulated ourselves and dropped a trap into the hole. It stopped before going through the ice.

We had dynamited, dug, cut, and shoveled, but we had still broken only a small hole through the bottom layer of ice.

The house was thoroughly iced in by that time, and while we didn't want to break it loose, we couldn't dynamite with the house in place. The only way to clear the hole was by hand, using a twelve-foot pike constructed of two lengths of iron pipe with a sort of pike blade at one end. Fortunately, the house had a roof high enough to enable us to do this.

We secured our homemade pike to the oceanographic winch and, leaving ourselves enough slack, threw it like a javelin down into the hole. The winch cable was used to draw it up, ready for throwing again.

Someone in authority at the base heard about what we were doing and was concerned about the possible loss of the pike and its cost to the government. He suggested we attach a rope to the pike and wrap the rope around our wrists. The pike was, of course, attached by a steel cable to the winch, but perhaps the "troubleshooter" didn't quite grasp the problem.

When it finally rammed the hole, the pike went down like a locomotive, and the house shook from the jerk of the cable. We were happy we weren't lashed to it, but maybe the administrator knew something about us that no one had yet been rude enough to point out.

After a day and a half of chopping, we still had a large crust of ice around the bottom and a tremendous amount of loose ice in and around the hole. And the hole was still inside the house. Someone had a great idea: We would break through the ice crust with a "hole burner," a G.I. can with an air vent at the bottom and a tall smokestack. It is fired by diesel fuel dropping into the bottom of the stack.

We assembled the burner, dropped it down the hole, put on an extra stack, and fired it up. I checked the contrivance the first night, and all was well. The following morning we found the burner knocked askew, probably by a seal; because there had been no draft, the fire was out. In frustration, we secured everything with guywires and nails and returned to the base.

16
Fire, Fish, and Trained Seals

We saw smoke coming from the fishing house as we were heading there the next morning. A tracked vehicle of the McMurdo Fire Department passed us on the way, turned around, and returned to McMurdo Base. We continued on to the house to find it burning furiously.

Inside the house were ten gallons of fuel oil to run our heater and hole burner, three gallons of gasoline for the winch, and an oil-soaked floor. We didn't know whether they had caught fire and were afraid to open the door to find out; the rush of air might make things really blow up. Stan and John tried to quench the fire while I, because of the hazards, tried to stop them, when a big-wheeled Navy fire-fighting truck arrived. We watched tearfully as our fishing house–laboratory burned to the ground.

The Navy fire-fighting crew was efficient, despite the loss of the house. When they decided it was gone, they concentrated on preventing an even worse holocaust. Two 50-gallon tanks of diesel fuel on the side of the house had not caught fire, nor had two nearby five-gallon containers of gasoline. They slung a cable around the oil tanks and pulled them away.

Nothing was left of the fishing house but some iron framework, some metal scraps from the winch, and a **91** charred and dirty fish hole. We were discouraged. Although the hole was still open, the charring hindered ability to see into it, and the ashes in and around it clouded everything, including our optimism.

We were provided with another house—though not the shiny, new one we'd 'seen earlier—and moved it in over the charred fish hole, located another winch, and were back in business. Again, we decided, we would not put a hole burner in a fishing house without having someone on watch while it was operating. Hole burners were usually used the way we did, but it wasn't a safe procedure, as we found out. We also thought it would be a good idea if the Navy replaced the oil-soaked floor of our new fishing house before it too caught fire and burned all the equipment. They could not replace it, we found, but we were grateful the Navy was there and kept us in business.

We soon settled down again and started serious fishing. We used small hooks (size 8 or 10) baited with seal meat and sometimes could pull out two or three borches at one time. The problem was enticing them into the hole while they swam around underneath it. The most effective method had been learned from Art De-Vries the year before. One man would lower a shiny object deep beneath the hole and slowly pull it up, jiggling the line all the while. Hundreds of borches often followed the shiny object. Another successful method was baiting the hole with live amphipods, like little shrimp, which we caught in traps at the bottom of the sound. A bucket of these small animals dumped into the hole usually drew numerous fish. We also tried shoving meat scraps into the hole, flashing bright lights into it, and dropping a bright light deep into the water. Some of these attempts worked well.

Catching the fish by net in the fish hole didn't work very well for us, although we thought it should have. Borches are certainly curious and follow lures, so the actual capture of them shouldn't have been difficult.

Sometimes our luck was good and sometimes bad. And that, I know, is the story of all fishermen.

We tried trapping fish at the bottom of the sea, too, using a six-foot cylindrical trap weighted and slung so that it remained horizontal once in position under the water. It took a long time to raise and lower the big trap in deep water, though, because the cables sank faster than the trap and lines became fouled. On the return trip to the top, the winch had to be operated slowly to avoid damage to the fish; fish die if they are brought up too rapidly, just as a human diver gets the bends if he surfaces too fast. A trap could not be raised faster than 25 feet per minute.

Later we caught fish from the shore, from the sides of icebreakers, and after the ice had broken up in the austral midsummer, from other ships. Fishing was good from these locations, but we suffered the same problems that stateside fishermen have. We caught our tackle on rocks, Navy gear, and other people. Most days it was so cold that about a half hour of fishing was all a man could stand. Fishing in a warm fishing house is far better.

The god that looks after fishermen soon smiled on us at the house. The borches started to rise in the hole and a week later were present by the hundreds. One day we caught four hundred fish, with Stan Komatsu getting credit for more than half of them. Maybe spreading black ashes around a fish hole is the magic trick. Maybe we just lived right.

Besides the borches, we wanted a good catch of the big mawsoni, seldom seen because they live deep in the sea, to balance our studies on the comparatively small borches.

The mawsoni's predator in the food chain is the Weddell seal, one of the larger seals of Antarctica. He swims down, grabs the mawsoni in his teeth, and crawls up on the ice to eat. He makes his own holes for this purpose, usually, although he certainly couldn't in the thick ice we faced. When seals bring the mawsoni up to **93** the surface of ice, the fish are sometimes still alive.

After our successful catch of borches, we began having trouble with seals, which started using our fishing holes as holes for breathing. We hoped they might bring up mawsoni, but we didn't want them to interfere with the borch catches. We didn't want to scare them away, either, because we wanted their help with mawsoni after we had finished catching borches.

I have never been sure whether we actually trained the seals to bring up the mawsoni, but maybe we did. To our delight, at any rate, the seals started to bring them to us; as a reward, we treated them nicely, except for the wrestling matches required to get the big fish away from them. Whenever they appeared, Stan had friendly chats with them, to which they seemed to respond.

The various ways seals might be used for fishing have not been exhausted, I am sure. One way might be to bring seals in by helicopter from other areas when none are coming into the fishing-house area and to encourage them to stay. They might then become mawsoni hunters. The practice in 1966 was simply to wait patiently for a seal to take over the hole and begin to fish.

We had success in only two of the five years we fished for mawsoni with seals. Perhaps better rewards for the seals should have been worked out. But fishing is an inexplicable sport. If we knew all about it, it wouldn't be fishing, would it?

17
Penguins versus Man

With the start of spring, the Antarctic again came to life. Not only were the borches appearing in schools for their two- or three-week run, but the penguins were starting to lay their eggs at Cape Crozier.

John Bigler and I rushed to Crozier, leaving Stan to hold down the fishing house with the help of volunteers: some sailors and a few USARP field-party members who, because of bad weather, had been unable to get into the field. I was sure that Stan would always have a companion or two in the fishing house.

John and I arrived at Crozier about the third of November; I was delighted to be there again. Every year both the environment and the people change. In the close confines of a Jamesway hut, the people make all the difference between irritation and happiness. The previous year, both Roger Tory Peterson and Bill Sladen, two delightful companions, had been there. This year, Bob Wood was back again with Sladen's graduate student, John Boyd. With them were John Peterson, an engineering student who was our electronics expert, and Andy Anderson, a New Zealand mountain climber. There were six of us in the Jamesway hut, and it was a little crowded.

Two double bunks were set up in the front of the **95**

tent, and every night we put a cot on each side of our all-purpose table. John Bigler and I could not retire at night until everyone had left the table, and we had to get up before anyone stirred in the morning. We also had to borrow other people's bunks for catnaps during the day when we came in from a particularly hard task. But it was no hardship, really, because everyone was good natured about the inconvenience.

John Peterson was young and intense, and Andy Anderson, in his mid-fifties, was thoughtful and well organized. Both were great and both necessary to the success of our mission.

In private life, Andy was headmaster of a large school and an outstanding mountain climber. He had been selected as one of two New Zealanders to make the grand circuit of Antarctica and return to help inform the people of New Zealand of activity to the south. He rejected his VIP status, electing to participate instead. Andy had the wisdom of a true educator.

John Bigler and I immediately set about the work of collecting about a hundred and fifty penguin eggs. Our work was divided roughly into four categories.

First, we would collect fresh eggs to be separated into whites and yolks and frozen for transport to the United States for additional research.

Second, we would collect eggs for incubation to study embryo development. We wanted to see if we could specify the relationships between development and egg-white composition. We needed eggs that had been incubated for only two or three days and other eggs that had been incubated for about half the full period of 34 days. We would take both groups of eggs back to McMurdo to complete incubation in the laboratory. Some of the eggs would be opened at different stages of incubation to follow the biochemical changes of the egg white. Other eggs would be allowed to hatch, enabling us to feed the penguin chicks for several weeks. This last project wasn't really part of our main interests, but John thought we could do it and that the information we got would be useful to future researchers.

Third, we would inoculate a group of live birds with antigens that would cause the defense system of the bird to make antibodies in the blood. This would help Dick Allison, who was studying penguin blood proteins, identify the fractions of the blood serum that contained the antibodies. We planned to inoculate each bird two or three times, band them so that we could identify them later, and take blood samples at designated intervals. We wanted to wait at least a month after the first inoculation before taking any blood, to permit development of a high level of antibodies.

Finally, we would continue to investigate the mysterious presence in penguin eggs of a protein that combines only with riboflavin (vitamin B_2), although we hadn't been able to identify riboflavin in any egg whites. We planned to give the penguins large doses of riboflavin to see if it would show up in egg whites. It would be more difficult to work with penguins in the wild than with ducks or chickens in cages, but we experimented for several days before developing a procedure. We would give riboflavin only to the female penguin, ideally just before the first egg was laid, and then hope to see the vitamin in either the first or second egg.

Equipment for this research consisted of a long plastic tube with a bulb at one end, which contained the riboflavin preparation. We learned that once we got the tube into the penguin's throat, it was no problem to shove it down to its stomach. But getting it into its throat was a struggle. Understandably, the birds objected.

Which was the male and which the female penguin? Bill Sladen claimed he could tell the sexes easily by a cloacal examination, but we decided simply to give the riboflavin to all the birds. It wouldn't make any difference if we made a mistake, which we were sure to do. We reasoned that penguins would prefer this treatment to the cloacal examination, a procedure involving the inser

97

tion of a cold steel instrument into their posteriors. Inoculating the antigens into the birds was a relatively simple job once we learned how to catch the birds and hold them. The first day, luckily, we had help from Stan Komatsu, who made the trip out with us, helped us for a few hours, then returned to fishing at McMurdo.

I inoculated myself one windy day. I slipped while fighting a struggling bird, and a penguin-sized shot of antigen went into my arm. It was a fine quality bovine serum albumin, a blood protein of cattle, and one of the antigenic substances present in beef. But mixed with it was an irritant used only to stimulate antibody production upon injection for research purposes and definitely not for humans. I'm still waiting for some type of allergic reaction when I sit down to a beef steak.

One of our final tasks before returning to McMurdo was to take a blood sample from an emperor penguin the Johns Hopkins group had in a little pen down the hill. They had operated on the bird for one of their studies, inserting a transistor temperature probe under his skin, which sent signals to a small receiving set not far away. But the bird rejected the probe, and his weight dropped from about eighty pounds to sixty. So John Peterson and John Boyd decided to operate and remove it. The penguin's condition worsened. Heroic measures were called for. When the bird became unconscious, Peterson and Boyd tried to revive it. Peterson covered the penguin's beak with his mouth and blew air into the bird's lungs, while Boyd did chest manipulations. Unfortunately, they got out of rhythm; when Boyd was trying to get the bird to exhale, Peterson was trying to blow into its mouth. Something had to give, and it was the penguin—right into John Peterson. In spite of the noble example of science before self, the emperor penguin passed away. John Peterson said the penguin was the lucky one. One of my prized Antarctic mementos is a movie sequence of the entire operation. Boyd merits an Oscar for his expression at the finale.

We were on our way back to the hut when we realized that bad weather was setting in. The wind was roaring by the time we reached our quarters. It was the start of another three- or four-day storm, with several days afterwards of intermittent bad weather. We used the time to dissect the penguin. For the sake of olfactory decency, I won't describe those days in detail; we put the bird on the floor beneath the bunks at night and hauled it out on the table after breakfast to continue dissection. We, as well as the entire hut and all our clothes, smelled just like the inside of a penguin.

The egg collecting, the administration of riboflavin, and the antigen injections were all completed before the storm. Our plans were to make three or four trips to Cape Crozier, and we had figured on a five- or six-day stay for our first visit. But the storm held us up for an additional eight days. The delay wasn't critical for our work, although it was hard on Stan back at McMurdo. I decided if we were going to continue two simultaneous lines of work in future years, we should have four people on our team so that two could be at each place.

On the thirteenth day, the helicopters came. We gave the birds another injection, then took off for home base, our fishing house at McMurdo.

18
Chemical Warfare, Storm and Fire

Stan had things well in hand at the fishing house. But because he was working alone much of the time, only a few specimens had been collected, although there were lots of them nearby.

The frequency with which seals were coming up to the house without bringing fish with them was becoming a major problem. Apparently, seals fed right below the hole, keeping the schools of fish away. We sometimes went more than an hour without seeing a fish, then suddenly hundreds would appear. Only a few would be caught before they would disappear, to be replaced by a surfacing seal. The take was thus much lower than it should have been, and we obviously had to do something about it.

First we tried rapping the seal on the nose with a pole as he surfaced, but that didn't seem to bother him a bit. Then a scientist searching for marine organisms nearby suggested that when the seal next came up for air, we squirt him in the nostrils with a shot of ammonia. We debated using such a trick for a long time, since it seemed pretty mean. But, as biochemists, we knew that ammonia is a common agent for reviving people; we were sure the quantity of ammonia the seal actually got would be small because it would be washed away as soon as he submerged. Only a shock was needed to get rid of him. Equipping ourselves with a hypodermic syringe without a needle, we filled it with about three ounces of a strong concentration of ammonia. The idea worked wonders. When struck with the full amount, a seal gave a tremendous gasp, submerged, stuck his head out again for a breath of air, and disappeared. We had good fishing for several hours.

The following day the seal reappeared, and a second squirting was equally successful. We congratulated ourselves on achieving a biochemical breakthrough without damaging the seal.

The next day, it was John Bigler's turn to hang over the edge of the hole, syringe in hand. The seal's approach, as always was signaled by bubbles and departing fish. John was ready for him.

When the seal surfaced, John quickly gave him the full shot. But the seal had just begun to exhale, and John was directly over the seal. The entire charge blew directly into John's face. Unlike the seal, John couldn't submerge in the ocean. Stan and I pulled him out of the house and onto the ice, where we frantically scraped snow from the frozen crust to wash his eyes. I first feared that John had gone into respiratory failure, then became worried about damage to his sight. We were at least half an hour by snow vehicle from the main base, and our first-aid kit contained nothing for the eyes. We continued washing John's eyes with snow and rushed back to base as fast as we could. He suffered little more, fortunately, than a case of badly bloodshot eyes.

During this episode, it dawned upon me again that these young men were my responsibility, and that even the smallest of accidents can be severe under the circumstances in which we lived and worked. We ended our chemical warfare with the seal.

We were now catching between fifty and seventy-five fish a day, dissecting muscles, collecting blood, and keeping our laboratory operations going.

Our fishing was now interrupted once again. We had to return to Cape Crozier to inject the birds once more and to collect some of the eggs we had marked and left for continued incubation. We planned to go for two days, return to McMurdo, and go back later for two additional days.

On this occasion, the weather managed again to break up our plans.

Helicopter pilots like to fly over the Ross Ice Shelf at the edge of the land where the mountains are not high. To do so they must make a turn around the southern end of Ross Island, but the extra distance is worth it to avoid treacherous crosswinds and gusts that make the direct line of flight far more dangerous. This time, as was frequently the case, even the comparatively safe route was impossible to fly for four days.

Finally, we made the try. Two helicopters took off, one carrying badly needed field provisions and the other Stan and me and our equipment. At the lower end of the island, the pilot announced negative ground speed, which means we were flying just fine but weren't getting any place. Pilots don't like to fly without moving, so we went back to base.

The next day we tried again and made it. It was a good trip. As soon as we had landed, the pilot took right off again, fearing another shift in the weather. And shift again it did! Stan and I were stranded there for eight days, instead of the expected two. We were tent-bound with the same group as before, except that Stan was substituting for John Bigler.

Maintaining a supply of water is always a problem in Antarctica, and it's particularly difficult during a long storm. We had to go about thirty or forty yards uphill behind the hut, because closer by, the wind had blown away much of the surface snow. The alternative was a much nearer spot down the hill, but the snow there was mixed with penguin dung. We elected to go to the higher, harder, but cleaner area.

Two of us would go together, crawling on our hands and knees and dragging the shovel and bucket behind us because of the high winds. In crawling and in scooping up the snow we had to be careful that neither the flat part of a shovel nor the mouth of a bucket faced the wind. A sudden gust could carry both tools and men away. A shovel caught by the wind becomes a lethal projectile indeed. Each of us who served as water boys received some pretty good whacks with the shovel or the bucket, but we soon learned great caution in a seemingly simple task.

Once again our old enemy, fire, came to haunt us when our stove became flooded with gas and burst into flame. A dangerous enough situation for a camper in the woods, the problem is critical with a hundred-mile-an-hour wind tearing at the shelter upon which one's very survival depends.

Seizing the flaming stove, Bob Wood carried it out the door and away from the hut, where the wind soon extinguished the flame. Now that's a man!

During lulls in the storm, we completed our work in the rookery, and when the weather finally cleared, we returned to McMurdo. That was the last I saw of Cape Crozier that year, but the others went back later to bleed the birds once again.

I didn't know when I left the States that 1966 was going to be one of our most successful years for obtaining mawsoni. Stan Komatsu and the others caught about a dozen that year, six or seven of them alive and with hardly a scratch on them. Their capture from the seals proved to be one of the greatest improvements in technique during our Antarctic research.

Dave Osuga and I met, as planned, for a day in Christchurch. The next day, November 29, he left for the ice, and I started my journey home.

When Dave arrived in Antarctica, he joined John Bigler and Stan Komatsu. John stayed until the first week in January, Stan and Dave until the middle of February. **103**

My faith in my colleagues was thoroughly justified. They continued to keep the seals diving deep for the mawsoni and caught many borches, too. They also fished on the banks of McMurdo Base after the icebreakers arrived about Christmas time. The water there varied from only about 15 to about 50 feet deep, and they were able to catch fish of several species that we had not gathered while working in the fishing house.

John Bigler was left with the hatching and rearing of baby penguins, which proved to be a big job. John and I had started the incubation of eggs in a laboratory bacteriological incubator. He turned the eggs daily, as a penguin would, and 15 of 25 eggs hatched—not bad at all. Of the 15, seven survived until the experiment was ended ten days later.

The penguin chicks were kept in a brooder heated by a light bulb and fed ground fresh fish through a tube inserted in their throats. They took only a small amount of food at each feeding and shortly afterwards were ravenously hungry.

Near the end of the experiment, John was feeding chicks around the clock. Apparently he was a good nurse, for seven chicks gained weight and remained quite healthy.

The experiment ended when the men were ordered to move the penguins out of the laboratory and into an unused fishing house. The laboratory was supposed to smell nice for visiting officials! Early on the second morning after the move, an abrupt change from cold and windy weather to a warm and tranquil day occurred. The temperature mounted rapidly in their house, and the poor penguin chicks died of heat prostration. The experiment had progressed far enough, however, to prove it is possible to hatch and raise Adélie penguin chicks artificially.

I attempted, on my homeward trip, to bring a few live penguin eggs to California. The fertile eggs were to be transported in a small portable incubator that could plug into electrical circuits along the way. The NSF office in Washington insisted that a 110-volt incubator would be satisfactory, because aircraft were equipped to supply this voltage. It turned out, however, that the aircraft used a 400-cycle, rather than a conventional 60-cycle, system, which was useless for our equipment. Navy Seabees gave me enthusiastic help by making two additional portable incubators with different circuits available, but the embryos didn't survive. They died from overheating in Hawaii during an unexpected two-day delay.

Our plane was scheduled to depart from Hawaii for the continent late on the day of our arrival. The Navy liaison officer had approved a stop at Travis Air Force Base in California, but he was overruled by a superior officer who ordered the plane directly to Washington for the convenience of a high-level diplomat. I and a dozen other passengers who also wanted to get to California were left behind when protocol won the day. As the diplomat boarded the plane, he waved at me and indicated his delight that the plane was going to land in California! He had been able, he said, to arrange by telephone to have breakfast with friends in San Francisco.

The following morning he landed in Washington with all his baggage missing. His clean shirts, the attractive lady Navy public relations officer detailed as his escort, my embryos, and I were all together in Honolulu. I, no diplomat, was left with just my embryos and no way to get from Honolulu to Davis, California. But the military transportation personnel rescued us two days later by classifying me as a civilian military dependent. The classification of the embryos I never found out, but it would have made no difference. I had known the embryos were alive when we landed in Honolulu, but they did not survive the trip to Davis. The loss to me was only a small one, because we had proved at McMurdo that we could hatch and rear little penguins. I hated to admit, though, that I was beaten by red tape in all these attempts.

105

19
Research
in Other Fields

By 1967 our research programs were well organized and the laboratory at McMurdo Base well equipped to handle some advanced biochemical procedures. As much as I would have liked to work at other sites in Antarctica, our research programs required us to be at McMurdo where the best facilities were located.

Since I was teaching a new course at Davis that fall, I couldn't be absent in the middle of the school year and could not go to Antarctica; but Stan Komatsu and Dick Allison, who had successfully passed their Ph.D. qualifying examinations, could take a few months away from the University. It was important to me and to our programs to have two well-adjusted and well-trained men I could count on to get the work done. They were on the ice that year from the end of October until just before Christmas.

Their primary assignments were to continue working with the fish and to procure more eggs and blood samples from the penguins. They were also to start clotting experiments on fish blood. We had found that fish blood clotted rapidly and wanted to know more about why it did.

The biochemical mechanism of blood clotting is of great importance to medical science, and we hoped the planned experiments would give us some answers to its puzzling nature. Stan and Dick were to work primarily in the McMurdo laboratory (and in the fishing house, of course), but I denied the team the pleasure of staying at Cape Crozier for any length of time. With only two of them, the risk of being stranded by bad weather was too great. Only a small number of penguin eggs were needed, and they collected all they needed during a one-day trip to Crozier.

They were unsuccessful that year in taking mawsonis and concentrated instead on the borches and on another fish of the same species, *Trematomus bernachii*. Stan's greatest efforts were directed at the blood-clotting studies, which he did with great precision. Since we planned to continue the clotting studies with fish from the warmer waters of California, we needed a control subject to serve as a comparative standard in both places. Stan himself served this critical function, repeatedly bleeding himself both in Antarctica and in California. Scientists who work with plants, bacteria, or insects may well be envious of a control so readily moved from place to place.

On their way to Antarctica, Stan and Dick stopped for a week in New Zealand to obtain blood from some of New Zealand's penguin species. As always, the New Zealanders went to great lengths to help, and blood from four species was obtained. New Zealand penguins are much scarcer than those in Antarctica. They are harder to catch, too, because of the more difficult terrain. Egg hunting in Antarctica is made easier by the American helicopter.

My particular field of biochemical research in Antarctica is but one of many, many others. Scientists from all over the world brave the hostility of that unique continent to seek out more and more knowledge about our world and about why its living things and elements behave as they do. The scientific discipline that hasn't used Antarctica as a laboratory, either directly or indirectly, does not exist.

Intensive studies have been made of Antarctic insect life to determine how organisms can exist in the cold climate. Further studies have probed the behavior of such minute microorganisms as algae and plankton—themselves sources of food for huge mammals such as whales.

Botanists, for their part, seek to find out more about tiny Antarctic plants, how they got there and how they've managed to survive. Much is known in warmer climates of lichens, for example, but rare is the chance to study in unspoiled conditions these fascinating fungi that cling to rocks and cliffs and trees.

In the earth sciences, geologists and glaciologists have learned much in Antarctica about the glaciers and ice formations that cover so much of the continent. Oceanography, too, is a major field of study. What causes the peculiar behavior of the Antarctic Convergence, where water temperatures change from warm to icy cold in just a few miles? Do currents cause the change? The weather, its violence, and it effect on the rest of the world is under constant study by meteorologists. Weather stations are manned all year in many places by many countries, and information gathered is exchanged by nations whose ideologies are in violent conflict on other fronts. Heads of states may squabble elsewhere, but scientists work together in Antarctica.

Scientific endeavors undertaken at least in part in Antarctica have helped unravel many of the mysteries of the world in which we live. Research in the behavior of the magnetosphere, for instance, has uncovered many of the secrets of the aurora borealis (northern lights) and the aurora australis, its southern counterpart, both of which have devastating effects and influences on much of the equipment used in this electronic age.

Further, geologists and paleontologists have almost surely confirmed the existence of Gondwanaland, the supercontinent that millions of years ago comprised what

we now know as South America, Africa, Australia, and

Antarctica. They have also shown that the earth consists of continents that are still moving and are uncovering more and more proof that the earth is made up of tectonic plates that have always shifted from one point to another. Identifiable earthquake fault lines, where earth folds and changes occur, apparently are the borders of these moving plates. Paleontologists have found fossils that must have lived in torrid climates millions of years ago, while the discovery of coal indicates there must certainly have been vegetation that died and rotted.

To these many scientific studies must be added results and discoveries of more immediate technological nature: How travel by air is accomplished in a freezing environment. How clothing can be developed to protect efficiently against cold. How vehicles can function under extreme conditions. How housing and food preservation can be improved. Not the least interesting of all the findings have been the effects of cold and solitude and adversity on man.

20
A Bitter
and Beautiful Land

Men are affected by environment and experience in many ways. In Antarctica, the effects seem intensified, and despite the hardships and extremes of living, most men want to return. Perhaps they are drawn by the companionship of fellow workers all coping with the same difficulties, or perhaps it is the physical characteristics of the continent itself. The challenge of a "new frontier" may beckon with its novel opportunities for research and discovery. Whatever the lure, Antarctica draws men back.

Man learns to respect and fear nature's strength in Antarctica, for the awesomeness of its energy is frightening. If all these natural energies were unchained and released at one time, the earth and everything on it would disappear instantly. It is a concept that makes man's nuclear destructive power seem pitifully small.

The first things a visitor to Antarctica sees are the high mountains. An experienced traveler once flying with me along the Transantarctic Mountains was moved to comment, "The mountains! My God, they are everywhere!" When one realizes that much of that land has never had a foot set on it by either man or animal, the effect is staggering.

The strong lashing winds shock the visitor even when he thinks he is prepared for them. He soon learns to respect the wind-chill factor, a figure, based on temperature and wind velocity, that shows how cold it *really* feels. If the temperature is 30°F and the wind is blowing at 40 miles an hour, for example, he had better prepare for weather that is 4 degrees below zero. On the other hand, if the wind is 40 miles and hour and the temperature is -30°F (a not unusual situation), he will be stepping out the door into the equivalent of 100 degrees below zero.

The ocean that surrounds this wild continent is also something fearsome. The strength of the tide is evident in the large treacherous cracks in the ice, caused as the ice expands and contracts as it rises and falls with the tides. The sight and sound of the rending and cracking of the thick ice near the shoreline will shrink anyone's ego.

The tremendous burst of life in the early spring is as impressive as the environment. Within a two-week period near the end of October each year, the spring storms arrive. That's when the Adélies, a third of a million at Crozier alone, swarm in from the ocean to make their nests; at the same time, fish and seals suddenly appear in abundance. The spring temperatures vary from -30 to above freezing (35°F), but they are usually between -10° and 10°F. The spring winds are frequently clocked at much more than 70 miles an hour. The weather can change drastically in moments.

McMurdo Base is sometimes referred to as the "banana belt" by those who work in the interior, nearer the South Pole. To those who arrive at McMurdo in October, no description could be less apt, for October storms in the area are some of the worst in the world. McMurdo also has the ocean to contend with. A heavy soaking with sea water during a storm at temperatures well below freezing is an experience hard to reproduce anywhere else on earth.

If the gigantic awesomeness of nature in Antarctica has no effect on the visitor, its beauty and ever-changing **111** scenery surely will. Outstandingly beautiful are the cloud formations against mountain backgrounds. The sun appears to circle the earth during the spring, summer, and early fall months, and color changes on these mountains are indescribable. These changes, when supplemented by light forming and reflecting and diffusing through the clouds, are like multicolored phantasies. Mirages are often seen, with endless and magnificent effects.

All the little things that one finds when experiencing beauty are also there. Of particular delight to me were the different colors and formations of ice. Sea ice varies from steel blue to snowy white, with sometimes even a reddish cast caused by the presence of living microorganisms. Even while walking in the streets of McMurdo Base, I often found myself stopping to stare at the ice forming in little pools of melted snow. Not since my boyhood in the Middle West, when I gazed enraptured at icicles hanging from the eaves of my home, had I ever really *looked* at ice. But in Antarctica, I would stop and study the long crystalline lines appearing in the ice, wondering why they went this way or that and why they had that width or shape. As I moved from one vantage point to another, a host of lovely forms emerged. In fish holes, too, I watched whiskers of ice continually form around the edges as the holes were slowly freezing in again. The whiskers served as focal points for more solid ice, until eventually a solid layer of ice had formed. The whiskers took unusual shapes and, because of free ice crystals in the water moving in and out, sometimes seemed to be alive. The contemplation of ice crystals is a habit and a hobby I would recommend to all.

Most people have had the experience of walking into woods and seeing things they've never seen before and hearing things that previously went unheard. It happens even more in Antarctica. There are living creatures only near the sea, but all of Antarctica has many sounds. The whistling, singing, crackling, and thundering of the winds is a constantly varying symphony. At the ocean's edge, the cracking of sea ice mimics the strange sounds of marine animals, while waves and birds and seals add their voices to the medley. One can stand in one spot, moving just enough to generate warmth, watching and listening to the sea for hours.

The pleasure of being alone is becoming less available to all of us. Society makes privacy difficult and often impossible to maintain. Many of our homes are large apartment structures or are dropped side by side in large tracts; we live with constant noise; we bump into each other every time we turn around. The telephone is an essential servant, but it is also a strident master that screams at us and pulls us from creative thoughts.

A loner is usually in trouble, imagined or real, and is frequently considered a bit odd. An example of society's reaction to loners is found in the comments made about Admiral Richard E. Byrd, as related in his book, *Alone*. Byrd wrote that when he undertook a monumental experimental venture—the operation of an all-winter camp in Antarctica to take meteorological observations—he was sharply criticized.

Byrd's winter camp was originally designed for three men, but he was unable to provision it for more than two. He decided it would be better for him to be alone, since he believed that three could get along in crowded quarters while two would probably have difficulties.

Gossip charged him with deserting his command at the main base. There were also comments that he was going alone because he was a secret alcoholic. The admiral was going off to sit and drink in a hole cut in the ice for several months! If the stories had been true, he wouldn't have lasted more than a few days. How harsh can society be?

Sir Charles Wright, my helpful friend from Skyland, was the victim of the worrying and fretting of the Navy administration during a recent visit to McMurdo. How I enjoyed a private evening's hike with Sir Charles around the periphery of the base. But this was not enough for Sir **113**

Charles, who got up early the next morning and hiked the ten miles alone to Williams Air Field before breakfast. What an image would have developed for the Navy if something had happened to this great scientist and explorer with all the modern conveniences at their disposal. And, besides, Sir Charles was more than twice the average age of the Navy officers at McMurdo.

Of all my experiences in Antarctica, probably the best of all were the many weeks I spent at Cape Crozier. During the later years, when our penguin work was relatively light, I deeply missed the longer stays at Crozier.

Mostly I have missed the isolation of the hut with only two or three other men, and the wonderful combination of hard work and camping out. I often hiked alone over the hills to mark and survey penguin nests. To stand on an Antarctic mountainside in howling winds and watch leopard seals and flying birds and penguins is emotionally exhausting. But to me it was one of the greatest thrills of my life.

Living quarters near penguin rookery at Cape Crozier.

Thanksgiving "dinner party" in hut at Cape Crozier, 1966.
From left, author, Bob Wood, John Peterson, and John Boyd.

Adélie penguins, Ross Island.

Author at Adélie penguin rookery, Cape Crozier, 1964.

Emperor penguins, Cape Crozier, 1969.

Emperor penguin with chick
in "fur pocket."

Creche of emperor penguins, Cape Crozier, 1969.

Cutting away frozen egg white from emperor penguin egg.
Author (on left) and Jerry Hedrick.

Bill Bridge demonstrating method
of digging a snow cave to USARP
Survival class, 1969.

Weddell seal and pup lazing in Antarctic sun at Hutton Cliff,
thirteen miles from McMurdo.

21
The Emperors
and Hallett

In mid-October, 1968, I returned again with a larger group. Two students were undergraduates from the University of California at Davis—James Norris, a math major whose second major was in wildlife, and James Moore, a sophomore pursuing a general letters and science curriculum. I had selected these young men with great care, and I was certain that they would do their work well. They did not disappoint me. A third member of our group was Augusto Trejo Gonzales, who had joined us at Davis after graduating from the Mexican National University with a degree in biochemical engineering. Gus was a well-built, stocky, young Mexican. His English was picturesque, and we thought Antarctica would be a good place for him to brush up on standard English. Gus and his English both turned out well.

In addition to these three, I brought two senior people with me. One was Dr. Frank E. Strong, associate professor of entomology at Davis. Frank had applied for a project of his own, working with insects, but it was not possible that year; he went along with us to be better qualified to handle his own program in Antarctica the following year. Frank was a great help to me. He was an experienced camper who had spent a lot of time roughing it in Alaska while in the military service. He was   **121** also an old friend. I had been his father's (Professor Frank M. Strong) first graduate student of biochemistry at the University of Wisconsin in 1938. I had known Frank as a small boy.

My other senior colleague was Dr. Jerry L. Hedrick, an associate professor of biochemistry at Davis. We were working together on the muscle enzyme phosphorylase, and Jerry was an expert in the chemistry of phophorylases. He was a great help in getting things going in the laboratory as well as in the field.

In operations like this, there are always hangups. The six of us arrived in Christchurch ready to go on the ice, but there were no physical clearances for Gonzales or Hedrick. Jerry Hedrick and I were to stay only five or six weeks, so any prolonged delay would cut out a major portion of our time. Nevertheless, we had to leave the two of them at Christchurch, waiting for the medical papers to filter down through Navy channels. They arrived on the ice a week later.

Emperor penguins were on our hope list that year. We had asked NSF to consider possible ways of getting emperor penguin eggs in mid-winter (May or June) from the emperor rookery at Cape Crozier. Unfortunately, the logistical problems had not been worked out for such a hazardous trip during the Antarctic night.

We initiated a program which we called "operation ice archeology," the purpose of which was to collect frozen emperor eggs. We knew that frozen eggs would not be as useful in our studies as fresh eggs, but we hoped they would be satisfactory for biochemical studies of evolutionary relationships.

To be useful at all, the eggs had to have most of the original properties of the egg whites, except those that would be changed by freezing. They would have to be frozen without more than a day's incubation by the bird, have become covered with snow to prevent evaporation, and have come to rest in a place not frequented by birds, so that the eggs would not be crushed.

Each of the existing 1,500 adult emperor penguin pairs produces only one egg a year, so the chances of finding many eggs with the characteristics we needed were small. Nevertheless, we made a superficial inspection of the rookery to see if the idea was feasible. On the first try, we actually found one egg; it proved to be quite satisfactory for our comparative and taxonomical biochemical purposes.

During this trip, we visited Cape Hallett about 400 miles north of McMurdo, for the first time.

Hallett has its own beauty and uniqueness. The station was originally established as a joint venture of New Zealand and the United States, and the buildings were erected right in the middle of an Adélie rookery. This didn't seem to bother the Adélies at all, for they wandered around the streets of the town just like people. The station was run by a complement of about a dozen sailors under a chief petty officer who called himself the Mayor of Hallett. The self-given title was purely honorary, however, because when it was his turn to do the dishes, for example, he fell to along with the others.

Cape Hallett is a beautiful place, with mountains over 12,000 feet high all around, towering icebergs frozen in the sea just a few miles away, and flashing color on the mountains that ring the station and the bay.

The only reason we got to Hallett at all was due to a communications blackout caused by the disruption of radio waves by cosmic energy fallout. There was no communication between McMurdo and any other base, including Hallett, and certainly none between McMurdo and Christchurch. Weather forecasts, so important to our living patterns, could not be made, and most of the radio-guided operations of planes were stopped. All the planes used in USARP operations were grounded except for one experimental group flight, and we became part of that flight.

We had two C-130 (Hercules) planes for the weekend and another for part of the time. One served as the transport plane and the others as guiding aerials. The two aerial planes circled overhead, one near McMurdo and the other over Hallett, and messages to and from McMurdo and Hallett were relayed back and forth. The operation worked smoothly, but I am glad I didn't have to pay the air fare.

22
Whiteout and
the Shock Treatment

Our stay at Hallett was cut short. There was, on the one hand, some concern that the weather might worsen to the point that no plane could come for us. On the other hand, there was the possibility of a break in the communications blackout, and if this occurred, the big backlog of essential transportation that had built up in McMurdo would certainly have priority over our needs. Only two of us, plus a guest, had gone to Hallett, and we were far less important than the large field parties waiting to start work in geological programs or exploration surveys in the interior. It was essential to get those people, many of whom were already several weeks behind schedule, on their various ways.

If the weather got worse we could be stranded for up to three months at Hallett, for the air strip was only a cleared area on sea ice of the minimum thickness (five feet) on which the Navy could land a C-130 plane. Further melting of the ice could cause the strip to be closed, and the only transportation from Hallett would be by icebreaker several months later.

When we learned, on the second night after our arrival, that a plane was coming again to Hallett, we wrapped up our gear in time to make the return trip to McMurdo. As it turned out, there were two more planes **125** before the airstrip was closed for the season, so we could have stayed for four more days.

We landed at Williams Field in a strong crosswind at about 2:30 A.M. I'm certain that the Hercules, a wonderful plane, could land in the middle of a hurricane! There were two trucks waiting at the field to take us the ten miles back to McMurdo Base. Jerry Hedrick and I, along with one of the members of the plane's crew, went in one truck, and the other Navy men and our visitor went in the second one.

A few miles from the airstrip, the road leaves the ice shelf and goes some 60 feet out onto the sea ice, continuing along offshore until it reaches the base. While we were on this stretch, the storm became more intense, with snow blowing parallel to the ground and visibility approaching zero. We found ourselves, as a consequence, in one of the greatly feared polar whiteouts, during which there are no shadows by which to judge distances and no horizon.

Pilots especially dread these whiteouts, because what sun may show through the low-hanging clouds is reflected with the same intensity by the snow, so that the pilot can't possibly tell how far he is from the ground at any time. His altimeter is not accurate enough to give him the precise measurements he needs, and the term "flying in a bottle of milk" is not exaggerated. We, at least, could tell where the surface was, because we were on it.

Less than half an hour after we started we were lost, and our truck was mired in the snow. We knew we were within five or six miles of McMurdo Base, but we didn't have even the slightest idea of the general direction we should take to get there. We had no radio, and at 3 o'clock in the morning, we knew most of the men at McMurdo would be asleep. We were tired and worried men!

We were able, finally, to dig ourselves out. We hoped that by continually turning slightly to the right we would either come back to the ice shelf or find land. We could only pray that we wouldn't go through a hole in the ice as we neared the shore.

There is always great danger near the shore, because the ice frequently buckles from pressure at this point, and sometimes actually breaks off, leaving a space of clear water. We feared that if we should come across one of these danger spots, we might not see it in time. We crept along, hoping that if we did slide off into the water, we could escape the vehicle in time.

Suddenly the air cleared a bit. We could see Observation Hill at McMurdo through the blowing snow and knew we were in a comparatively safe area at last.

At about the same time, Frank Strong, who had been waiting for us, appeared in another truck, having come in search of us. Within 20 minutes we were at McMurdo Base in a greatly contrasting world. The sun was shining and there was very little blowing snow. It was like a beautiful Christmas morning in the Middle West.

Over the frozen ocean we saw what appeared to be a dense cloud of very thick white smoke, about 30 feet high above the ice—the whiteout we had just been in. Above it was a nearly clear sky!

In our fishing operations in 1968, we concentrated on getting blood serum from the borches and on capturing the big mawsoni. We were trapping from the bottom and fishing at the surface.

Once again, we were invaded by seals. But instead of using ammonia, as we had done so unsuccessfully the preceding year, I developed a shocking device using a simple induction coil. It gave a jolt that a person could easily withstand under normal dry conditions.

When a seal surfaced, we gave him a shock on the nose. It worked well enough to keep seals away, allowing us to catch a lot more surface fish. Unfortunately, the safety aspects of the new device were less than desirable, for salt water is an excellent conductor of electricity. When a seal came up to the hole, splashing sea water all over the place, the shocking device became highly dan- **127** gerous. I decided that either we had to stop using it entirely, or that only I could operate it.

Shortly after I took over use of the shocker, I knocked out a seal so completely that he was unconscious for several minutes. That convinced me that we should either develop a new method of chasing them away or make friends with them and learn to live together.

My decision to make friends with the seals was partly prompted by a communal bath a seal and I enjoyed in the fish hole. I had done exactly what I told my students not to do, particularly when alone in the fishing house. I fell into the hole while waiting to shock a seal lurking below. The seal quickly disappeared. Luckily, I was able to grasp the cable and throw myself up onto the floor of the house, soaking wet and nearly frozen. I quickly peeled off my clothes, huddled against the heating stove, and was soon in good shape again. That was when I really decided to get along with the seals, rather than try to impose my will on them.

Frank Strong left the Antarctic after completing the preliminary investigations that would prepare him for his visit the following year. Soon it was time for Jerry and me to depart, leaving our three students behind until Christmas.

Just before we left, we began finding pieces of mawsoni in the fish holes, and I was sure it would be a great year for catching the big fish. It was.

All three students worked hard, but Jim Norris became the most dedicated mawsoni catcher of them all. He set up a cot right next to the fish hole, although the cot made it impossible to open the door. Jim would lie waiting there at night, completely clothed, for ten hours at a time. Apparently he and the seals got along together splendidly, because he caught half a dozen mawsoni.

Jim and his seal got along so well, in fact, that it reached the point where the seal came up and stared at him, face to face, from a distance of 18 inches. Jim claims he adjusted to the seal's breathing as a mother does to her baby's cry; he would awaken as soon as the seal rose in the hole and began to breathe.

In addition to missing the mawsoni again, I missed another event I'd have given a lot to see. A general with more stars on his shoulders than could be counted came to inspect our laboratory. Inspections in the Antarctic, as elsewhere, are usually only "visits," but everybody knows that when high-ranking military men pop in, it's best to assume that you are being inspected and have everything as spit and polish as possible to avoid problems from Washington.

This time the men had only a few minutes' notice of the general's visit; it happened to coincide with the time that Gus Gonzales was taking his bath at the sink in the laboratory—an unauthorized place for personal ablutions, by any military standard. Gus's baths were rituals, accompanied by happy Mexican sounds, yelping, and other hullabalooing that made them joyous and drenching affairs.

When the men heard about the general's visit, they rushed to get Gus out of sight—out of clothes if necessary. They found him standing by the sink, covered with soap from top to toe, just before the general came through the front door to see scientific research being conducted in Antarctica. The men helped Gus put on his clothes, lather and all, and wiped the soap off his face; he leaned over the sink busily examining something— probably his fingernails—as the general nodded approvingly and went on his way. (Gus' version is much less colorful!)

My return trip was the usual pleasant passage through New Zealand and Honolulu, but apparently I left a small wake behind me.

I had been asked by several members of Navy Air Group VXE-6 to obtain a stuffed Adélie penguin for their museum in the United States. I had obtained half a dozen penguins that year for our blood studies and supplied the carcasses to other researchers, so I agreed I **129** would give the skin of one to the Navy men for mounting.

But how would I get the penguin to the museum? It would be difficult to have it stuffed and mounted in New Zealand because of agricultural and veterinary health laws and regulations concerning the conservation of Antarctic species. We decided that a VXE-6 plane could transport a frozen penguin from Christchurch to Alameda Naval Air Base in California, where I would have it skinned and mounted and shipped to the VXE-6 museum in Rhode Island.

The pilot of the plane was Commander Edward Feeney of the U.S. Navy, and the USARP office had great difficulty accepting the statement that two Feeneys were carrying one penguin to California. It was considered most probable that one Feeney was carrying two penguins. After all, the government had many reports of millions of penguins in Antarctica, but they knew of only one Feeney. Somehow, Commander Feeney cut through the red tape, and two Feeneys and one penguin had a happy meeting at the California air base. As far as I know, that penguin is still an important exhibit in the museum.

The Ross Sea phase of our 1968–1969 program ended with the arrival of the three students at Travis Air Force Base on December 23. Within a few days, I was again going to the airport, this time taking someone leaving for Antarctica.

On December 27 I drove Dr. Arthur DeVries, who first taught us how to fish through the ice, to the Sacramento Municipal Airport. He was flying to Washington, where he would transfer to a military plane that would take him to Punta Arenas, Chile. This was the prelude to a month's program aboard the National Science Foundation's new research vessel, *Hero*. Art also sailed to Palmer Station on the Antarctic Peninsula, where he obtained several varieties of fish specimens for our program. So, in that one season, we had research coverage from both ends of Antarctica.

As I watched Art's plane take off, I wished fervently **130** that I could be going with him.

23
The Ladies Arrive

In 1969 our crew again numbered six. We had two students from Davis with advanced technical training as chemists: Jack Vandenheede of Belgium, who had completed his first year of biochemistry, and Steven Chan of Hong Kong, who had worked in our laboratory during the summer and early fall prior to our departure. Jim Phillips, a graduate student in history and environmental science at Sacramento State College, also accompanied us. They were the three "worker boys" for the season.

We were also accompanied by Dr. Richard S. Criddle, associate professor in the Department of Biochemistry and Biophysics at Davis. Dr. Criddle came along as Jerry Hedrick's replacement, to help us with certain specialized types of work and to act as troubleshooter. The five of us arrived at McMurdo about October 20.

The sixth member of the crew was Dr. Frank C. Greene, who came in for a little over a month. Frank was a former student of mine, who completed his doctoral research on the Antarctic material in our laboratory. He had been unable to go to Antarctica before, but that year he successfully obtained leave from the U.S. Department of Agriculture in Albany, California. No one ever saw a more inspired Antarctican!

We found many improvements and changes in pro- **131**

cedures, equipment, and environment. One was an atomic reactor, which supplied power for base operations and for a desalination plant, which made potable water from the ocean. The latter greatly increased the amount of water available to us. We could take three times as many showers! It did away, finally, with the fire hazards of the diesel-oil snow melters.

We also had a handsome all-metal dispensary and a two-story, all-metal housing unit for the USARP workers, with toilets and showers all in the same building. There was a large dining facility, part of a prefabricated building for the wintering-over crew. Transportation was markedly improved, and the big C-141 Starlifters flew directly from Christchurch to the United States.

Our group was hardly off the plane before we were making our first trip to Cape Crozier to hunt for emperor penguin eggs. We made three trips and found five eggs, of which three appeared suitable for our biochemical studies.

The egg-hunting expeditions we made, however, not only were very different from the trips of the early explorers but were completely unlike the dog-sledging trip that New Zealanders had made only a few weeks earlier. Three of the New Zealand wintering-over party from Scott Base, together with an American medical doctor, Lieutenant Commander Pace, U.S.N., left for Cape Crozier in the middle of September and returned to Scott Base eleven days later. Their total travel time was about seven days, in addition to four days at the Cape. What a difference between that and my three visits by helicopter. The comparison made me feel spoiled. They were confined to their tents for three of their days at Crozier owing to a furious Antarctic storm.

The New Zealander's dog-sledging days were not beautiful sunlit ones with dogs mushing over picturesque snow-covered ice. Their trek was more in the tradition of Scott, Amundsen, and Shackleton, with high winds, snow, and the hard sweaty work of helping dogs pull the heavy sledges. I was very grateful for the two eggs they brought back—more than I was for the five we obtained in comparative comfort. New Zealand grows men.

On the days between flights to Cape Crozier we got our fishing houses ready. We planned to place one over deep water and another over shallow water near shore. Fortunately, the Navy helped us cut the one over the deep water. Since the sea ice had not gone out during the previous summer, we had two years of accumulated ice to challenge us; it was 12 to 13 feet thick at the spot we wanted our fishing hole.

This was the first year the Navy had the two-foot drill I've mentioned. The cluster of five cores they drilled for our first hole meant about a ton and a half of ice we didn't have to remove by hand, much of it in a pit 12 feet deep.

We blew out the walls between the cores of the first hole with blasting cord and then dynamited out the bottom. It worked perfectly, but we were left with a ton of loose ice and another ton of sea water that had to be removed by hand. We worked from 9 A.M. one morning until 5 A.M. the following day. As the end of the job approached, we were so tired and pleased that we got sort of silly about it, pushing one another and falling and sliding on the slush and soft ice. It was like a kids' snow fight, only a lot wetter and colder. I forgot all about fragile joints and wobbly vertebrae.

The hours we spent preparing our ice hole and pulling the fishing house into position were well worth the effort, for we began to catch borches immediately. They were running heavily, and our timing was perfect.

The biggest change in 1969 was the arrival of the first women scientists at U.S. stations in Antarctica.

Four young women arrived about three hours before our annual Halloween party. They were from Ohio State University and planned to collect soil and geologic specimens in the dry valley near Lake Vanda, across McMurdo Sound on the mainland. They were Dr. Lois Jones, the **133** geologist and group leader, Mrs. Kay Lindsay, Mrs. Eileen McSaveney, and Miss Terry Lee Tickhill. They didn't arrive at the party until rather late, and their arrival was, of course, of historic importance to the shaggy and goggle-eyed males.

The presence of women had many ramifications. A number of years earlier, one of the commercial airlines had allowed stewardesses to go to the main base for a short time. Most of the Navy men stayed away, I have been told, because they feared their adjustment to the absence of women might be undone.

Another time, a half dozen women had been aboard the NSF research ship *Eltanin* in the seas near Antarctica and apparently had fared quite well, but there were only fifteen times as many men aboard as women. At McMurdo, we had about a thousand men and only a few women. Apparently the women fared satisfactorily. The Navy men and USARPs also survived.

The wisdom of sending in a few women can be argued, I suppose, and I am in no position to know whether it was the best thing for the NSF to do. I would have preferred sending in a hundred WAVES to ease the male-to-female ratio.

The young women and I had met at the 1969 orientation conference at Skyland, but it wasn't until afterwards that we became acquainted. The USARP representative, Ken Moulton, was faced with a housing problem, because the new quarters were not yet ready for occupancy. When the women arrived, several "more mature men" were left in the senior scientists' quarters, which had been designated for the women. Four double rooms were assigned to the eight men and two double rooms to the women.

My personal introduction to the women was on the second night, when one of them sewed a red patch on my black windbreaker trousers. I had the honor of having the first woman-patched pants at McMurdo. All the newcomers were bright, cheerful, and interesting.

My alcove was opposite that of two of the women, which caused me to awake each morning to the sound of girlish noises. Would you believe that those sounds were even more pleasant than the sounds of penguins at Cape Crozier? The presence of women at McMurdo caused a number of problems. One was the posting in their quarters of the official NSF list of safety rules relating to exposure to cold. The first item on the list stated that great care should be exercised in touching metal objects, to which the skin of bare hands might freeze. The second item stated that, if freezing to a metal object did accidentally occur, an immediate remedy was to urinate upon the part frozen to the metal. The third item stated that one therefore should not pick up any item higher than one could urinate upon!

During the first few days at McMurdo, even when they were viewed from the rear at 100 yards distance, they caused many a man to stare. From that distance what was inside the red parkas and windbreaker trousers could have been an admiral!

Shortly afterwards, when Jim Phillips and I were back at Cape Crozier for a few days work, I found Dr. and Mrs. Dietland Muller-Schwarze, along with Bob Wood and three other young men. The Muller-Schwarzes are a highly talented husband and wife team of biologists from the University of Utah, who were spending parts of two Antarctic summers at Crozier conducting experiments in penguin behavior. Their findings have contributed considerably to our knowledge of Adélies and their living patterns. They returned to McMurdo for a few days' visit while Jim and I occupied their slots at Crozier.

It was great to be at Crozier again, but I realized that Antarctica had changed. The hut had been considerably enlarged from the size I had known during my first years and was now protected by a heavy plywood outer shell. It had experienced its first woman occupant, for which NSF had supplied a much superior and separate sanitary facility. The magnificent exposed throne was still there, but now a respectable and completely enclosed old-fashioned outhouse for women was placed alongside it. The new one had been prefabricated at McMurdo and brought out in sections by the helicopters that brought Jim and me. I had the pleasure of "stoning it down," a process consisting of piling small boulders around it to keep it from blowing away, then participating in its formal christening. What a whooping and hollering there was!

Cape Crozier was just as beautiful that year as it had been in previous years. Jim Phillips and I, not being blessed with the bad weather that so often delayed arrivals and departures, returned to McMurdo on schedule. The good weather denied us a longer stay at that exquisite place.

24
Helicopter Crashes

Fishing for borches was a big success in 1969, with several thousand fish going through our complete biochemical sampling procedure. It was another off year for the mawsoni, unfortunately, because the seals did not use our fish hole to breathe through. We tried putting in a second hole complete with a house, but it didn't work. Within 30 minutes after we had blown the second hole clean, a seal rose, looked us over, and disappeared. He was the first and the last. Many times we could see their big bodies flashing just beneath the hole, but none ever surfaced again, and we never saw a mawsoni that year.

Traveling between the two fishing houses and McMurdo Base increased the hazards of transportation. Although the distance was only a few miles, frequent whiteouts caused our inexperienced crew to become lost several times and my beard to become a little grayer.

Once, one of the crew disappeared while walking ahead of the snow vehicle as a guide. A second crew member tied a long nylon rope around his waist, with the other end attached to the vehicle, then walked in a great circle around the truck as far as the rope would extend. He found the missing man heading in the wrong direction, towards the north end of the island and the open sea. This happened only 500 yards from the edge of the **137** ice, on the road leading up the hill toward the base.

Serious accidents plagued the Navy that year. One helicopter accident resulted in the deaths of two civilians and injuries to two other civilians and three members of the Navy crew. The helicopter had a motor failure about 50 miles from the base. As it started to descend, slowed by the resistance of the rotor to the air, it was blown into the side of a mountain where it crashed and burned. The pilot, Lieutenant Commander Brandau, was badly burned while helping others escape the flaming wreck. Only two weeks earlier he had suffered a fracture of a facial bone when he fell on the ice helping some of the Johns Hopkins group with their emperor penguins.

The accident was reported to McMurdo while we were eating supper. The administrative officer, who thought I was a medical doctor, called me from the table to help the five injured and burned survivors, who had been picked up and were arriving at the landing pad. I couldn't help much with the actual receiving but I did what I could; I learned how seriously the pilots took their responsibilities of flying the choppers through the dangerous mountain passes in nearly impossible winds.

The rescue functions of the Navy's Antarctic Development Squadron 6 are little known outside Antarctica. One of their jobs is to maintain a pararescue team of specially trained parachute jumpers. Each member is a volunteer and must complete an arduous training course in Antarctic survival and mountaineering.

Many Navy men have played important parts in my trips on the ice. I knew the air squadron best, since they were the ones who took us on our travels. One was David B. Eldridge, Jr., who was a lieutenant when I arrived the first year; during my last year he was in charge of air operations and held the rank of Commander. Another, Captain Eugene W. VanReeth, commanded the air squadron that helped the two Feeneys and the penguin get to Rhode Island. Twenty or thirty other fliers and

138   support personnel became close friends of mine over the years. Dave Eldridge, called the "Big E" because of his 6-foot 6-inch frame, spent much of his time talking about how half the Navy spent its time flying out over the mountains to help Doc Feeney make a penguin egg soufflé.

Bill Bridge, a New Zealander and my roommate at one time, was once picked up, following an accident, by a U.S. helicopter that got lost in a storm but eventually carried him safely to New Zealand's Scott Base. As an experienced mountaineer and rescue man, Bill felt that New Zealanders should do something in exchange for the many times Americans had helped his countrymen. As a consequence, he organized an instruction course, bringing in about six men every year from New Zealand to teach survival, crevasse scaling, icecraft (how to climb and cross glaciers), and rescue work. His course was so effective that even men who had never been on the ice before became highly skilled at the techniques he taught them after only a week or two of training. No one can know how many lives Bill Bridge saved through his teaching.

Another helicopter was wrecked two weeks after the first one when its motor stalled when it was only a dozen feet off the ground. The injuries, fortunately, were limited to sprains and bruises.

The Navy airmen were again grounded when the ski-equipped undercarriage of one of the big C-130 Hercules was smashed during a landing in a whiteout.

My good friend, Dr. Fiorenzo C. Ugolini of the University of Washington, apparently irritated the Navy one night by pitching his tent between the chapel and the admiral's quarters. He had just arrived after being picked up by a helicopter from a distant valley, where he had been camping and studying soil chemistry.

Ugolini was quartered in a billet with men waiting to be shipped into the field, who were understandably idle and noisy. After trying to sleep, he arose, got out his field tent, and pitched it in a quiet spot outside next to the **139** chapel. Despite eviction orders from the officer-of-the-guard (and how many other officers no one knows), Ugolini wouldn't budge. After considerable argument and loud commands, the chaplain solved the problem with Solomon-like wisdom: "Some sleep inside the church on Sundays during my sermons, so why can't someone sleep outside it?"

Older Navy officers remembered that six years before Ugolini had received a Navy commendation for saving the lives of a helicopter crew. He had been camped on the mainland about 150 miles from McMurdo when a helicopter crash-landed directly on his tent. He struggled out of the wreckage of tent and helicopter and calmly gave first aid. So far as the Navy was concerned, Ugolini could do no wrong, and the word was passed along to all hands.

The Ugolini campout helped me a few nights later when I set up quarters in one of the USARP warehouses. I had just returned from Cape Crozier with a mildly raspy throat. The tobacco smoke in my quarters had set me coughing, so I unrolled my Crozier gear in the warehouse and went to sleep on the floor. About 2 A.M. a Navy guard attempted to evict me, but he retreated when I stated that I was another one of Dr. Ugolini's group.

25
Last Trip

My trip to the ice in late 1970 was a sad one, because I knew it would probably be the last to the land I had learned to love so much. This time, however, I would live in a modern two-story building with almost a private bath, where I could use a sauna every night. I would have all the creature comforts I needed, and my work would be much more effective because of the well-equipped laboratory that was now established. The sauna sounds like a luxury, but if you try working for many hours covered with frozen ocean spray, you will understand its medical values and its contribution to a degree of comfort.

Many of the changes were more subtle. A larger and older polar office of the National Science Foundation could not help but have many of the problems that affect a bureaucratic organization. Men who had once been active field researchers were now loaded down with administrative tasks. Public-relations officials were assuming a more evident role. The scientist pursuing his own project was harder to find amidst the large well-organized projects, which resulted, I believe, in more activity but less creativity.

Our crew in 1970 included Jack Vandenheede, Steve Chan, and me, as the oldtimers, and three talented young **141** men who had not previously been to Antarctica. One was Dr. Gary E. Means, who had received his Ph.D. in biochemistry from my laboratory two years before. Gary was another student who couldn't go with me before because his research was tied to his bench at Davis. The other two students, Ahmed Ahmed and Charles Ho, were in their second year of graduate study in biochemistry.

On October 3, we put Jack, Ahmed, and Charlie on the first planeload of scientists headed for Antarctica from Travis Air Force Base.

Six days later I received a telephone call from the NSF headquarters in Washington telling me to inform friends and relatives that the young men were safe. One of the first planes from New Zealand to McMurdo had run into a bad storm and had crash landed in a whiteout at Williams Field. Fortunately, there were no fatalities on the plane that crashed, although there were many injuries. It was only later that I learned my group had missed that plane and had flown on another one.

Gary made the trip about three weeks later and I arrived a month after that.

Through a quirk in the simultaneous timings of a scientific conference in Germany and departures of the military planes from California to New Zealand, I made my last trip to New Zealand by traveling around the world enjoying the luxuries of commercial airlines. It was cheaper to keep on going once in Europe than to return. What a difference from my first trip on a military plane with boxed rations, no stewardesses, and no windows. I not only attended the biochemistry meeting in Germany, but had two weeks of scientific discussions in Israel and Australia, as well as pleasure stops in Greece and Hong Kong. Most Australians easily understood my crisscrossing the earth in order to stop for a month's work in Antarctica, and many others along the way easily accepted it, but there were a few who appeared to think I was part penguin to have made such a globe-circling trip.

142   The Navy flight from Christchurch to the ice was a jolly one, thanks to the New Zealanders going to Scott Base. My seatmate was a young American Naval officer, Dr. Neal Thomas Peterson, enroute for twelve month's duty as the wintering-over physician on the Rockefeller Plateau, Marie Byrd Land, about 800 miles from Mc-Murdo. He started our conversation by telling me that he had once applied twice in the same year to go to Antarctica. A serious car accident involving him and two other Naval medical officers near Narragansett, Rhode Island, was responsible for his double application.

The three officers had all been accepted for wintering over, and were making their final preparations when the accident occurred. Dr. James Mathias, who was to have been the physician at McMurdo, was killed. Dr. Michael Green, who was to have been the dentist, received such serious leg injuries that he was disqualified. Dr. Peterson was himself so critically injured with crushed bones in his head that his death was considered inevitable, and a replacement for him was obtained. He made such a miraculous recovery, however, that he was soon on his way. He told me he believed there was a relationship between his intense desire to visit Antarctica and his rapid recovery. It would be interesting to know the private opinions of his medical superiors when this young man applied twice for a long cold stay in Antarctica.

Women had broken the Antarctic ice in 1969, and in 1970 two women were actually living beneath the surface of the snow at Longwire Station, an isolated geomagnetic research installation located "twelve miles from downtown Byrd" according to Ray Heer, the director of atmospheric physics for the National Science Foundation.

Dr. Irene Peden, associate professor of electrical engineering at the University of Washington, Seattle, had directed an Antarctic research program on atmospheric physics for several years, but this was the first time she had actually been to Antarctica. She and an assistant, a young Kiwi woman, Julia Vickers of Christchurch, **143** worked for about a month at Longwire. They traded their turns with the men to climb up a ladder and shovel snow for an additional turn of cooking and washing dishes. Irene's proclamation was, "Equal is one thing, the same is another, and they are different."

I had hoped to arrive on the ice at mawsoni time but as I found out, I was really not needed that year. Nor were there any mawsoni for me to capture from the seals. The students had done such a thorough job that all I could provide was another pair of hands, and those only after all the really heavy work had been completed. As to the mawsoni, we had another dry year. Several times we lost heavy tackle to some large underwater creatures. These were probably mawsoni, but lost fish don't count. Our record stood at two good years out of five.

My stay of slightly over three weeks soon ended, and three of my students and I prepared to return home, leaving Gary Means behind.

Two days before our departure, the Navy safety engineers closed the ice road from McMurdo to our fishing houses because the ice was melting and tidal cracks were starting to appear. They permitted us to use our snow vehicles if we did so quickly, but we had to dig out our houses and tow them back to land. I was slightly misty-eyed when we did this—the houses were filled with years of memories of great times. I was sure I would not return the following year.

On the afternoon of our departure, I prepared for a final hike across the ice to the remaining fishing house two miles away, where the others were still working. Just as I was getting ready to go, the NSF office told me that we could no longer use the snow vehicles on the ice road, which meant there was no way to bring back the fishing house. They were prepared to let the house and the snow vehicle go to sea.

Chris Sheperd, the USARP representative, told me later that my daily walk across the fissure-ridden ice had **144** been worrying the Navy safety officials. I suppose they had allowed me to continue because I had made six trips to the ice and had the status of an old Antarctican. Besides, I would be leaving soon and would be out of their hair forever. I thought of Sir Charles Wright and I knew how much he, too, enjoyed his illegal walks on the ice.

In Christchurch we were met by the new USARP representative, Dr. Richard Penney, an old friend and biologist—the man, in fact, who had stabbed the leopard seal when he was attacked on the edge of the ocean. We had a happy reunion and were joined by Steve Chan, who was on his way to McMurdo. Steve and I compared notes about the project and how it was going; once again our scheduling plans had worked out as we had hoped they would.

The trip back to California was typical. We developed plane trouble and were grounded for a day at Honolulu, where I cut my foot while enjoying the beach at Waikiki. What a way for an Antarctican to finish his work!

26
Visits to
Scholastic Pinnacles

The Antarctic program was going very well as the end of its seventh year approached. But a number of unrelated matters then caused me to stop the field phases of the work and to take an academic sabbatical. Most important was paying my debt to my family. We had only had one real vacation in eight years. They had been a major part of the reasons for my successful Antarctic trips. Without their help, forebearance, and patience, it would not have been possible to conduct my Antarctic program. My daughters were at the right age, mature enough to enjoy and profit by living in a foreign country, but not too old to prefer to go alone. So we went to Europe for a year's study and work.

A university professor's sabbatical is almost a sacred adventure. According to academic custom, the sabbatical is supposed to be used by the professor for intense academic study, to make him a better professor when he returns. In other words, it should be a period of renewal. Biochemistry professors usually go to some famous biochemistry department or institute where they can engage in undisturbed research, but I also had my deep and abiding interest in polar science. Happily, both interests were satisfied, just as they had been in Antarctica itself, and we spent four months in Cambridge, England, followed by nearly six months in Zurich, Switzerland. Four years previously I had attended the dedication of the new wing of the Scott Polar Research Institute at the University of Cambridge. I knew that the Institute was a center of activity for polar scholars and a meeting place for polar researchers and explorers; there was also a very famous university department of biochemistry.

Cambridge proved to be the best marriage of my biochemistry and Antarctic interests I could have possibly found. On the one hand, I had an appointment in the department of biochemistry with an outstanding biochemist in my field, Dr. H. B. F. Dixon, and on the other, I was given an office and the run of the library at the Scott Polar Research Institute. My family and I spent four fine months there, I enjoying stimulating biochemical and scholarly polar activities, and my family, the Cambridge University town environment.

The Scott Polar Research Institute was founded in 1920 as a memorial to Captain Robert Falcon Scott and his companions. It started as a place where polar travelers and explorers could meet and where items of polar interests might be collected and stored. Now an international center for polar research and scholarly reference, its functions are to collect available information on those regions, to stimulate and sponsor interest in polar regions, and to participate in the general teaching activities of Cambridge University. The Institute consists of a library, research laboratories, a research organization, a museum, a lecture room, and staff members who are teachers at the university. Someone who had learned I was going to be associated with the Institute said, "Such a British museum and library must be a real musty place." This is far from the truth. The spirit of Scott lives in it, and its reference works are studied by young and old alike. Nearly every day of the year there are visitors from all parts of the earth, many of whom are polar workers or polar explorers. I must have encountered a hundred interesting people during my stay. A half dozen or more of them I had met on the ice in Antarctica. Even Bill Sladen popped in one day.

To me, the highlight of the year was the British version of the American Skyland planning conference, held at the Scott Polar Institute. Suddenly I was again in the middle of a large group of young men full of enthusiasm about Antarctica and busy with preparations for imminent departure. The British operations in Antarctica are different from ours. Their programs are almost entirely staffed by government employees, most of them attached to the British Antarctic Survey. These men usually go to the ice for two years. Thus only half the complement changed each year. The head of the Antarctic survey in 1970 was Sir Vivian Fuchs, the famous British explorer and Antarctic expedition leader.

The heart of the Institute is its staff members and students. These combined the vigor and fascination of polar exploration and science with the excellence of Oxbridge (Oxford and Cambridge Universities). Some of these people I got to know well; others I only had a short acquaintance with, because they were soon off to polar activities, in both Antarctica and in the opposite polar region. I would have given much to have followed some of these fellows on their many expeditions that year.

The director of the Scott Polar Research Institute was Dr. Gordon de Quetteville Robin. Dr. Robin started with an early interest in Antarctica, as he was born in Melbourne, Australia, where many Antarctic ships have their supply port. In World War II, he was a submarine officer with the Royal Navy and, from 1946 to 1948, was in charge of the Antarctic installation at Signy Island in the Falkland Islands Dependencies; for the following three years he was the senior physicist with the Norwegian-British-Swedish Antarctic Expedition. Dr. Robin became director of the Institute in 1958. As I walked with him to have lunch at his college, I am sure that some of the undergraduates thought he was an armchair philosopher walking with an uncouth old American. The latter,

148

of course, would have been right, but the former very, very wrong.

Polar buff though I was, a lucky friendship with another Institute staff member introduced me to areas of Arctic polar science and lore that were brand new to me. Terance Edward Armstrong had a background very much like Gordon Robin's. In World War II he was a parachutist in the British Army, and had since seen polar services in the Arctic regions, particularly polar Russia. He has been assistant director of research at the Institute since 1956. It was from Terance that I got a gift—the idea of spending my retirement years in learning about, and perhaps even visiting, some of the remote but inhabited areas of the Arctic. I had never really given much thought about what I would do in retirement, because, with a young family for my age, I had always believed I would "die with my boots on." Boots or no boots, Armstrong's world beckoned!

Another new idea for me was the concept of traveling underneath a massive ice pack in a submarine, as Dr. Charles Swithenbank, the leading scientist on the British Royal Navy's first submarine surfacing through the ice at the North Pole, had done.

It was in Brian Birley Roberts that I found a fellow bird man. Like the others, he was an old polar scientist. He started earlier than most, in fact, and was active in the Arctic in 1932 and 1933; he was with the British Graham Land Expedition on the Antarctic peninsula in 1934–1937. His record is long and impressive. Brian spent half his time at the Institute and the other half as administrator on Polar International Relationships for the government in London. He was truly a part of the university. His apartment overlooked the middle of the "backs" at the river. As I sat on several occasions at his main window sipping sherry and watching students (frequently engineering students practicing their art), he would tell of his love for stimulating young people to participate in the real world of oceans, birds, whales, mountains, and ice- **149** bergs. I have been only one of very many who have knocked and will knock on that apartment door and who will be welcomed with his cheerful enthusiasm towards life.

The scholastic side of my work was in the hands of the librarian, H. G. R. King. His book, *The Antarctic*, had just been published, and he gave me lots of good pointers. Here also was intense enthusiasm and love for polar subjects, as well as for his profession. Ever since, whenever people comment to me about the dullness of work in libraries, my answer is "go visit Harry King at Cambridge."

The students at the Institute were just like the staff members except, of course, more varied and perhaps more curious about everything. They were working on ice physics, geology, Siberian history, and at least another half dozen subjects. But they were also part of the spirit of the Institute. One of them donated his nonscientific talents to the Friends of the Polar Institute. This organization provides a means of allowing many individuals to keep closer contact with the Institute. This they do by receiving the Annual Reports of the Friends organization and of the Institute and its work. Furthermore, the Friends' subscriptions provide funds used to help preserve the valuable archives and museum collections. The money from subscriptions is also used in other ways, such as support of occasional publications. How could anybody resist sending in his guinea after reading this student's poem:

All hail to thee whose missive comes
Borne on the wings of poesy!
For by expending trifling sums
Thy future can be rosy!
For if one pound and five new pence
Are from thy pocket coughèd
150   A bounteous cup of great events

Can thenceforward be quaffèd.
          Good friend, for Godde's sake essay
          To read the pamphlets I purvey,
          For if a guinea thou would'st spend,
          Thou canst become a Polar Friend.

For haply whilst in city pent
Or in some noisome alehouse
Thy cagèd thoughts have oft been bent
To austral seas where whales spout;
Where stormy petrels dance on waves
And southern stars embrace us,
And seals are sent to wat'ry graves
By grampuses voracious.
          Vicarious are such thoughts, I wot;
          But are they worthless? Not a jot!
          For if these musings should thee suit
          Then join the Polar Institute!

Peter Wadhams
Scott Polar Research Institute
Cambridge University

The soft life of my first year completely away from the Antarctic program finally got the best of me. My back gave out! This was the same back ailment I had fought so many years and had secretly nursed throughout each trip to Antarctica. But I had not gone through my usual routine of vigorous exercise and had not done all the tricks I knew would keep the problem under control. Then, of course, I hadn't gone to Antarctica at all, so by the middle of November I was in bad shape. When I found I couldn't buy a traction apparatus for home use in bed because of restrictions of the English Government Health Service, I placed a rush order to my doctor in California and patiently waited in pain. The British postal service must have thought a machine gun was being imported from California, for after long delay, I learned it had **151** been held several weeks for inspection. The apparatus helped repair my problem, but the biggest help came from renewed exercise and from the understanding of Institute people. Not sympathy, but understanding. They all knew that a good polar dog suffered from his bumps and bruises and needed time to lick his wounds.

A month and a half later, although only half recuperated, I set off on the second part of my sabbatical. Again, some sort of polar ray must have shined upon me! I was fortunate to have another good blend of polar science and an academic environment in beautiful, crystal-clear Zurich, Switzerland, where I became affiliated with the Swiss Federal Technical University. I'll never again make any jokes about the gnomes of Zurich. The department of Agricultural Chemistry of the university funded a series of lectures on protein chemistry, the amount making up my salary loss, with a little bit left over. I worked much of the time in the department of Solid State Physics, in the laboratories of Professor W. H. H. Granicher, one of the world's great authorities on ice physics. In what better place could I do research on antifreeze glycoprotein from Antarctic fish blood? Two of the good Swiss scientists, Dr. Hansa Ahrends, twice a refugee from other European countries, and Dr. Robert Hofmann, were not polar scientists, but they were excellent ice and crystal physicists. I soon felt very much at home with them.

Ahrends and I worked with his sophisticated equipment for precise measurements of heat evolved when liquids crystallize. We had hoped to show that the antifreeze functions by slowing down the formation (nucleation) of seed crystals of ice, but we could not do it.

I therefore switched to watching television. There were no Swiss murder mysteries on my programs, only ice crystals. Hofmann, a crystal-structure microscopist, designed an elaborate temperature-controlled setup on the state of a microscope, equipped so that the image was projected on a television screen. I spent many hours in front of this screen watching the freezing and melting of solutions of the antifreeze. We proved that solutions of the antifreeze froze nearly a whole degree centigrade below zero, but melted at the normal temperature of zero. Crystals of ice floated for hours without melting or freezing at temperatures between freezing and melting points. In contrast, water or solutions of other glycoproteins froze or melted when the temperatures were either a few hundredths of a degree below or above zero.

After a fruitful six months, my family and I were ready, at the end of June, to return to California. In the interim, I learned that my sabbatical had truly broken a chain of events, for our NSF program in Antarctica would now definitely be no more. During that year, Dr. Arthur DeVries had been back to Antarctica to work on antifreeze protein, and several of my other Antarctic friends were carrying on the work with penguins. Just as it should have been, polar research was continuing without me.

27
What We
Accomplished

My laboratory is but one small part of the Antarctic scientific programs. Our investigations, like all the others, are far from finished and probably never will be. Studies of the material we collected must continue; we have only helped point the way for future researchers, who will have far better resources, equipment, and knowledge.

It is difficult for any scientist to make an objective appraisal of what he has accomplished. His work is always reviewed critically by his scientific peers, and he is influenced by their adverse comments as well as by their praise. As cumbersome as scientific literature may seem to the layman, publication of a scientist's work not only reports his work to his colleagues but may help some future researcher know more about his subject and relieve him from having to go over the same ground again.

In protein biochemistry, I believe my colleagues and I made several substantial contributions to the complex studies of the chemical properties of proteins and of their biological functions and roles in the substances that make life processes work, not only in birds and fish, but also in man.

My interest in going to Antarctica had roots deep in the foundations of my life-long research and teaching **154** career. I had wanted to study the species living in Antarctica because I believed I would find secrets in their proteins. Someone once called me a "molecular mechanic," and I wanted to have a look at the mechanics of the protein molecules of the creatures living in such a cold and faraway place.

What is a protein that it should so attract my interest for so long and lead my students and me to the bottom of the earth? Proteins are one of the most important of the half dozen main substances of which living materials are built. Proteins are important because they serve many critical functions in living organisms. In fact, enzymes (which are proteins) are catalysts, which synthesize most of the complex materials in life. In other words, proteins are the constituents that make life "tick." Other substances, like nucleic acids, carry the life code from generation to generation, and still others, like fat and carbohydrate, carry energy. But the work of life is done by proteins.

Proteins are large biological molecules that probably exist in trillions of different structures. Yet they are made up of just a small number of building blocks, the amino acids, of which about twenty exist. But these amino acids can be looked at like letters of the alphabet, which we can structure and rearrange in different ways to make words and sentences, all of which have different meanings. This is the way it is with proteins, which usually contain two to three hundred amino acids arranged in a linear chain. Some have many more of one amino acid than others have, and the orders of the amino acids are different. The amino acids carry different meaning to the protein, just as the letters of the alphabet carry different meaning to the large imagined words. Amino acids have different charges—some positive, some neutral, some negative. Some amino acids are what chemists call "water-loving," while others are "water-hating." Positive and negative groups of amino acids will tend to attract or repulse one another, and water-loving and water-hating groups will tend, respectively, to get together with water or try to get **155** away from it. This causes the long polymer of the protein molecule to fold up in different ways, frequently into a structure resembling a loosely wound ball of string. The water-hating amino acids, for example, usually tend to curl up inside the molecule to be next to one another and away from the water in which the protein works in the living cell. The water-loving ones tend to be on the outer side of the loose ball of string.

The relative numbers and kinds and positions of amino acids in protein polymers are thus responsible for the protein's shape, as well as the way it reacts to environmental changes. Yes, proteins react to their environment very much like a living material will react, although they are just a part of the living material and not really living themselves. When the temperature is changed in the cell or in a solution of the protein, the protein may change its shape; it may even unfold, depending upon the particular protein and the amount of temperature change. In addition, and most important to living systems, a protein with enzymatic activity is folded in such a way that it is able to work as a catalyst. With many enzymes, it is the way in which the different amino acids are folded to make a "catalytic area" that makes one enzyme a catalyst for one chemical reaction and another for a different one. Other proteins, which are not enzymes and hence not catalysts, have other functions, such as helping carry oxygen in the red blood cells. This is what hemoglobin does. Still others are quite strong, rigid, and even water repellent, and are present in such structures as skin and hair.

My main interest has been in what the protein chemist calls the relationship of protein structure to protein function. In other words, I want to know how the orders and positions of different amino acids are responsible for the different properties and functions of proteins. In some proteins, changing just one amino acid in the polymer chain (out of a total, say, of 250 amino acids) may cause the protein to be nonfunctional, if it is an enzyme, or to perform its function very differently, if it is nonenzymatic. Protein chemists try to relate the role of each of these amino acids to the way the protein works. Some are interested in how it might change the action in a catalytic center of an enzyme.

In my particular case, I have had a long interest in the effect of temperature on the properties and actions of proteins. In general, changing temperature causes the protein to undergo minor changes in properties, as long as the temperature is kept within the "reasonable" limits of its original environmental temperature. Such variation would usually be plus or minus 5 to 10°C (plus or minus 10 to 20°F). Even these changes sometimes cause large effects on the protein. At more extreme temperatures, particularly higher ones, drastic effects may occur, such as coagulation of an egg when it is boiled. This coagulation is a result of what the protein chemist calls denaturation—literally "going away" from the natural state. Obviously, the change is very drastic and almost always results in the destruction of the distinctive properties and function of the protein. Changes may occur in varying degrees at low temperatures, too, but changes at lower temperatures will usually reverse themselves, albeit slowly, when the protein is warmed back to its usual temperature.

In our study of proteins, my students and I have used two tools primarily. The first has been chemically changing the properties of the different amino-acid building blocks in a protein, without denaturing or breaking up the protein, to study what effects the chemical changes have upon the protein properties. Sometimes we have tried to change one amino-acid side chain into something which looks like another one—another of the natural ones, that is. A second main tool in our research has been comparative study of the structures and properties of similar, closely related proteins in different species. In other words, we use the changes provided by nature. My group has studied, for example, the different birds, **157** different mammals, and different fishes. Likewise, we have studied the egg-white albumins and transferrins of different birds. This is done because nature changes the amino acids in the proteins; if the species are closely related, the changes may be very small. We have developed a program of trying to use the changes made by nature to help us see the importance of particular amino acids in certain positions in the protein. Sometimes the changes cause extensive effects on the properties of the proteins, while at other times the effects are much smaller. These small effects are also interesting to us, since they usually are of lesser importance to the properties of the protein. So we can win even when we don't find anything! The Antarctic program was a particular extension of this comparative program.

Our original objective in studying penguin egg-white proteins was to find out whether they were sufficiently distinctive to make them useful in studying the relationships of penguins. The two objectives are not necessarily related, but we had success in both. The egg white proved to contain two proteins extremely useful in our overall study of how proteins work. One was transferrin, a protein nearly identical to the one in blood serum in humans and birds and involved in iron metabolism. The transferrin molecule can transport two iron atoms at the same time, but each iron atom is attached at a different place on the protein. For over fifteen years we had been studying human and chicken transferrins trying to find out how the iron was bound and whether the two iron-binding places in the molecules were different. The penguin egg-white and blood-serum transferrins were found to exist in four or five different structures, that is, to have multiple forms. Why should such an important protein exist in multiple forms? Was it important to its function in binding and transporting iron?

Another useful penguin protein was ovomucoid, which is an inhibitor of digestive enzymes. The penguin

158　ovomucoid was found to inhibit an enzyme in a way that no other inhibitor could, and we were trying to find out the reason for this powerful effect. These and other studies have since been supported by the National Institutes of Health.

In studies of the ability of some fish to survive in subfreezing temperatures, we have made much progress, even though we certainly haven't yet found the answers to this complex problem. When we started studying fish, we wanted to find out if any general characteristics of fish proteins made them different, since they had to exist and function in the very cold temperature of ice–salt water. We chose to examine the enzymes in the muscles and blood proteins of the fish, continuing the theme of our studies with penguin and human blood proteins. We initially chose four muscle enzymes that had been extensively studied in the muscles of warm-blooded animals and humans. We hoped to draw on existing information for help in our studies and to obtain knowledge that might be useful in understanding how the enzymes from the warm-blooded species work. Before we finished the work on muscle enzymes, we added three more enzymes —one from the heart, one from the liver, and one from the brain—to our repertoire.

In each of the seven fish enzymes studied, there are one or more characteristics that may be valuable in helping understand how enzymes function in warm-blooded animals, including humans. We found that each of the fish enzymes always functioned efficiently at the temperature of ice water, yet each of the enzymes showed many different responses when we attempted to make them work at higher temperatures. This shows that nature can adapt to environmental changes in many different ways. One of the enzymes worked well at the temperature of ice water, for example, but completely lost its function when warmed to the temperature of the human body. Another enzyme functioned well not only at the cold temperature of the fish, but also at the temperature of the human body.

159

When we compared enzymes from warm-blooded species with the corresponding enzymes in cold fishes, we found that some of the "warm" enzymes would not work efficiently at the cold temperature of the fish, because several of the "warm" enzymes, inhibited in the cold by concentrations of certain materials normally present in the cell, were not affected at warmer temperatures. Some of the "warm" enzymes were tested in the absence of these materials, and they functioned as well as had the "cold" enzymes at the cold temperatures. The fish enzymes were not inhibited by these materials at either cold or warm temperatures. They apparently had acquired resistances to inhibiting substances in the cold, a necessary acquisition if they were to function at the temperatures of the icy seas! Temperature adaptation was thus sometimes an adaptation to the presence of normal cell constituents that would be otherwise harmful in a cold environment.

Our main studies on fish blood proteins were with the antifreeze proteins, which prevent the blood from freezing at ice–salt water temperatures. We have devoted a tremendous amount of study to this antifreeze protein over a seven-year period, and three of my graduate students—Stan Komatsu, Jack Vandenheede, and Ahmed Ahmed—have written Ph.D. theses on aspects of this research.

The antifreeze protein may prove to have great importance in helping to understand the physics of ice, for our studies indicate an unusual effect of these proteins on ice-crystal formation.

Whether the results of research merit the effort and expense involved normally can't be answered until long after the work is completed. We know that the results of other non-Antarctic contemporary research in biochemistry are, at the moment, more valuable than ours, but we hope some of our results may point the way to new directions in new areas of research.

160   The Antarctic environment offers a natural laboratory for studying life in the cold. Current interest in global and space environment is focusing attention on the way living things perform and survive in extreme environmental conditions, since men, animals, and plants may have to live and grow in much colder climates and under unheard-of conditions in the world of the future. Studies in Antarctica may provide us with knowledge of how it might be done. Our studies on penguins may help in future "avian husbandry" and survival of this multimillion polar bird population; our studies on fish may have technological applications in future farming of the oceans.

Scientists hope their efforts will benefit mankind, and they know there can be no progress in technology without advances in the basic sciences. We hope time will show that we have contributed to both.

28
The Future

What will be the future of the magnificent frozen continent called Antarctica? It depends on how men use past and future discoveries, for science is moving so rapidly that totally new technologies for traveling to and within Antarctica, and for living there, will doubtless be available within a few decades.

The principal question of the future may well be one of international cooperation. The Antarctic Treaty is effective for only thirty years, and much of that time has already passed. The treaty has been far more successful than even its most serious and enthusiastic supporters envisioned. There has been little reason, so far, for men or countries to argue over the spoils of Antarctica, and it could well become a permanently international continent, with people of all nations living and working in the nearly perfect compatibility of the past and present. It could also be divided and redivided, however, in ways that would greatly lessen its usefulness to mankind. But the successful cooperation between nations during the first half of the Antarctic Treaty period is a good omen.

Antarctica has many physical characteristics that suggest an important future. Contrary to the popular belief that it is far off at the bottom of the world, it is actually only a few thousand air miles from any of the southern